G000016307

BOOK G

www.prim-ed.com

CURRICULUM LINKED

Teaching writing skills

Read — Analyse — Plan

Narratives

Recounts

Reports

Procedures

Explanations

Discussions

6266C

PRIMARY WRITING *(Book G)*

Published by Prim-Ed Publishing 2008
Reprinted under licence by
Prim-Ed Publishing 2008, 2014
Copyright© R.I.C. Publications® 2006
ISBN 978-1-84654-111-7
PR–6266

Additional titles available in this series:
PRIMARY WRITING *(Book A)*
PRIMARY WRITING *(Book B)*
PRIMARY WRITING *(Book C)*
PRIMARY WRITING *(Book D)*
PRIMARY WRITING *(Book E)*
PRIMARY WRITING *(Book F)*

This master may only be reproduced by the original purchaser for use with their class(es). The publisher prohibits the loaning or onselling of this master for the purposes of reproduction.

Copyright Notice

Blackline masters or copy masters are published and sold with a limited copyright. This copyright allows publishers to provide teachers and schools with a wide range of learning activities without copyright being breached. This limited copyright allows the purchaser to make sufficient copies for use within their own education institution. The copyright is not transferable, nor can it be onsold. Following these instructions is not essential but will ensure that you, as the purchaser, have evidence of legal ownership to the copyright if inspection occurs.

For your added protection in the case of copyright inspection, please complete the form below. Retain this form, the complete original document and the invoice or receipt as proof of purchase.

Name of Purchaser:

_____

Date of Purchase:

_____

Supplier:

_____

School Order# (if applicable):

_____

Signature of Purchaser:

_____

Internet websites

In some cases, websites or specific URLs may be recommended. While these are checked and rechecked at the time of publication, the publisher has no control over any subsequent changes which may be made to webpages. It is *strongly* recommended that the class teacher checks *all* URLs before allowing pupils to access them.

View all pages online

Website: www.prim-ed.com

Primary writing

Foreword

Primary writing is a series of seven books designed to provide opportunities for pupils to read, examine and write a variety of text types; narratives, recounts, procedures, reports, explanations and discussions.

Titles in this series:

- *Primary writing* Book A
- *Primary writing* Book B
- *Primary writing* Book C
- *Primary writing* Book D
- *Primary writing* Book E
- *Primary writing* Book F
- *Primary writing* Book G

This book is also provided in digital format on the accompanying CD.

Contents

Teachers notes

Six text types have been chosen:

- narratives
- recounts
- procedures
- reports
- explanations
- discussions

Three examples of each text type are given for pupils to read and analyse.

Following each example, a framework is provided for pupils to use in planning and writing that text type.

Each text type is presented over four pages:

~ teachers page

~ pupil page – 1 includes an example of the text type

~ pupil page – 2 uses a framework for analysing the text type on pupil page – 1

~ pupil page – 3 provides a framework for the pupil to write his or her own example of the particular text type

Teachers page

The text type and number of the example are given.

The parts of each text type are given with relevant information for the teacher.

Teacher information provides suggestions for using the worksheet in the classroom and ideas for display, publishing, purposes for writing, appropriate audiences and the context in which pupils may be asked to write the particular text type.

Some examples of **language features** used in each text type are indicated. Also see pages vi – vii.

Answers are provided for pupil page – 2 where the pupils are analysing the text type.

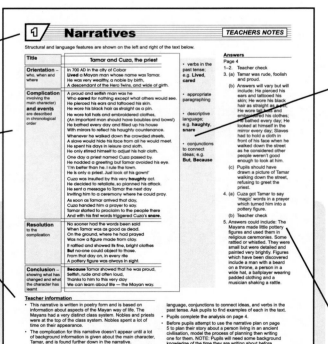

Pupil pages

The text type and number of the example are given.

The text type example is supplied.

Artwork appropriate to the example is provided.

Pupil page – 1

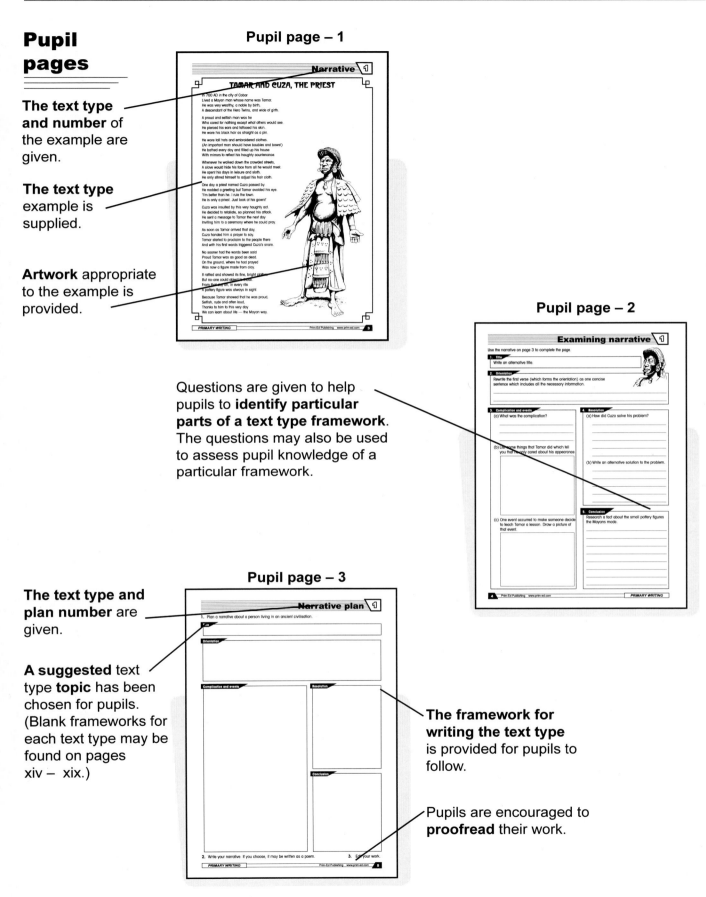

Questions are given to help pupils to **identify particular parts of a text type framework**. The questions may also be used to assess pupil knowledge of a particular framework.

Pupil page – 2

The text type and plan number are given.

A suggested text type **topic** has been chosen for pupils. (Blank frameworks for each text type may be found on pages xiv – xix.)

Pupil page – 3

The framework for writing the text type is provided for pupils to follow.

Pupils are encouraged to **proofread** their work.

• **Pupil page – 1** may be used at a later date to identify specific spelling, grammar or punctuation examples, as a reading comprehension activity or reading assessment.

Writing format information

Below are general descriptions of the text types included in this book.

Report

– is a framework which describes aspects of a living or non-living thing in detail
– includes:
  • **Title**
  • **Classification**: a general or classifying statement
  • **Description**: accurate and detailed
  • **Conclusion**: a comment about the content of the report (optional)
– uses the following **language features**:
  • factual language rather than imaginative
  • the third person
  • the timeless present tense
  • information organised into paragraphs

A report may be written in the form of a book review, scientific report, newspaper or magazine article, eyewitness account or a progress report.

Recount

– is a framework which retells events as they happened in time order
– may be factual, personal or imaginative
– includes:
  • **Title**
  • **Orientation**: all relevant background (who, when, where, why)
  • **Events**: significant events in detail
  • **Conclusion**: often with an evaluative comment
– uses the following **language features**:
  • vocabulary to suggest time passing
  • paragraphs to show separate sections
  • the past tense

A recount may be written in the form of a newspaper report, diary, letter, journal, eyewitness account, biography, autobiography or history.

Narrative

– is a framework which tells a story
– includes:
  • **Title**
  • **Orientation**: the setting, time and characters
  • **Complication**: involving the main character(s) and a sequence of events
  • **Resolution**: to the complication
  • **Conclusion**: often showing what has changed and what the characters have learnt
– uses the following **language features**:
  • a range of conjunctions to connect ideas
  • appropriate paragraphing
  • descriptive language
  • usually written in past tense

A narrative may be written in the form of a poem, story, play, imaginative story, fairytale, novel, myth, legend, ballad, science fiction story or modern fantasy.

Procedure

– is a framework which outlines how something is made or done
– includes:
  • **Title**
  • **Goal**: the purpose of the procedure shown clearly and precisely
  • **Materials**: a list of materials or requirements under appropriate headings or layout
  • **Steps**: the method in a detailed, logical sequence
  • **Test**: an evaluation (if appropriate)
– uses the following **language features**:
  • instructions often with an imperative verb
  • subject-specific vocabulary
  • simple present tense
  • concise language

A procedure may be written in the form of a recipe, instructions for making something, an experiment, an instruction manual, a maths procedure, how to play a game, how to operate an appliance, how to use an atlas or how to deal with a problem.

Writing format information

Explanation

– is a framework which outlines how something occurs, works or is made

– includes:

- **Title**
- **Statement**: precisely what is to be explained
- **Explanation**: a clear account in logical sequence of how and why the phenomenon occurs
- **Conclusion**: an evaluation and comment about what has been explained

OR

- **Title**
- a **definition**
- a **description** of the components or parts
- the operation—how it works or is made
- the application—where and when it works or is applied
- special features—interesting comments
- evaluation or comment/**conclusion**

– uses the following **language features**:

- subject-specific terms and technical vocabulary where appropriate
- simple present tense is often used
- linking words to show cause and effect
- information is organised into paragraphs

An explanation may be written in the form of an essay, or a handbook—for example, how a kite works—a science, health or geography text.

Discussion

– is a framework which argues for a particular position and attempts to persuade the audience to share this view

– includes:

- **Title**
- **Overview**: statement of the problem or issue and the writer's position
- **Arguments**: presented in a logical manner with supporting detail, usually from the strongest to the weakest
- **Conclusion**: a restating of the writer's position and a summary of the arguments presented

– uses the following **language features**:

- a variety of controlling and emotive words and conjunctions
- paragraphs to state and elaborate on each point

A discussion may be written in the form of an essay, a letter, policy statement, a critical review, an advertisement, an editorial or a speech.

Modelled writing

The role of the teacher is to observe and support pupils as they develop as writers.

Writing is an extremely complex activity, simultaneously involving decisions on content, text coherence and cohesion, spelling, grammar, punctuation and a sense of audience and purpose. Because it takes time and practice to develop understanding of the writing process and the different writing formats, many opportunities for pupils to interact with their teacher and their peers are essential.

Modelled writing is an effective way of supporting pupil writers, particularly when the focus is on the cognitive processes involved.

Frequent modelling of the planning process and how these plans can be used to write text in different formats, is strongly recommended.

Writing format checklists

Pupil **narrative** checklist

Title:

☐ The title is appropriate and interesting.

Orientation:

☐ The characters are introduced and described.

☐ Information about where the story happened is provided.

☐ The time the story took place is stated.

Complication and events:

☐ The complication involving the main characters is explained.

☐ The sequence of events is described.

Resolution:

☐ A logical, believable resolution is presented.

Conclusion:

☐ The narrative has a satisfactory ending.

Writing skills:

☐ The narrative is written in the past tense.

☐ Descriptive language is included.

☐ Vocabulary is varied and interesting.

☐ A range of conjunctions connects ideas.

☐ Paragraphs are used to introduce new ideas.

☐ Punctuation and spelling have been checked.

Name: _____ Date: _____

Pupil **narrative** checklist

Title:

☐ The title is appropriate and interesting.

Orientation:

☐ The characters are introduced and described.

☐ Information about where the story happened is provided.

☐ The time the story took place is stated.

Complication and events:

☐ The complication involving the main characters is explained.

☐ The sequence of events is described.

Resolution:

☐ A logical, believable resolution is presented.

Conclusion:

☐ The narrative has a satisfactory ending.

Writing skills:

☐ The narrative is written in the past tense.

☐ Descriptive language is included.

☐ Vocabulary is varied and interesting.

☐ A range of conjunctions connects ideas.

☐ Paragraphs are used to introduce new ideas.

☐ Punctuation and spelling have been checked.

Name: _____ Date: _____

Prim-Ed Publishing   www.prim-ed.com
PRIMARY WRITING

Writing format checklists

Pupil **recount** checklist

☐

Title: ☐ ☐ ☐ ☐ ☐ ☐ ☐ ☐ ☐ ☐ ☐ ☐

The title is suitable.

Orientation:

A clearly written orientation provides relevant information about who, when, where and why.

Events:

Significant events are described in detail.

Events are retold in chronological order.

Conclusion:

The ending is clearly described.

An evaluative comment about the conclusion is included.

Writing skills:

Paragraphs are used to show separate sections.

Descriptive language is included.

Vocabulary suggests the passing of time.

The past tense is maintained.

Sentence beginnings vary.

Quotation marks are used for quoted speech.

Punctuation and spelling have been checked.

Name: _____ Date: _____

Pupil **recount** checklist

☐

Title: ☐ ☐ ☐ ☐ ☐ ☐ ☐ ☐ ☐ ☐ ☐ ☐

The title is suitable.

Orientation:

A clearly written orientation provides relevant information about who, when, where and why.

Events:

Significant events are described in detail.

Events are retold in chronological order.

Conclusion:

The ending is clearly described.

An evaluative comment about the conclusion is included.

Writing skills:

Paragraphs are used to show separate sections.

Descriptive language is included.

Vocabulary suggests the passing of time.

The past tense is maintained.

Sentence beginnings vary.

Quotation marks are used for quoted speech.

Punctuation and spelling have been checked.

Name: _____ Date: _____

Writing format checklists

Pupil **report** checklist

☐ ☐ ☐ ☐ ☐ ☐ ☐ ☐ ☐ ☐ ☐

Title: _____

Classification:
A general or classifying statement about the subject of the report is included.

Description:
Accurate, detailed descriptions are provided.

Information is clearly presented.

Facts are relevant and interesting.

Conclusion:
A personal comment is made about the subject.

Writing skills:
Language is factual rather than imaginative.

The report is written in the third person.

The present tense is used.

Technical vocabulary and subject-specific terms are used.

Information is organised in paragraphs.

Punctuation and spelling have been checked.

Name: _____ Date: _____

Pupil **report** checklist

☐ ☐ ☐ ☐ ☐ ☐ ☐ ☐ ☐ ☐ ☐

Title: _____

Classification:
A general or classifying statement about the subject of the report is included.

Description:
Accurate, detailed descriptions are provided.

Information is clearly presented.

Facts are relevant and interesting.

Conclusion:
A personal comment is made about the subject.

Writing skills:
Language is factual rather than imaginative.

The report is written in the third person.

The present tense is used.

Technical vocabulary and subject-specific terms are used.

Information is organised in paragraphs.

Punctuation and spelling have been checked.

Name: _____ Date: _____

Writing format checklists

Pupil **procedure** checklist

☐ ☐ ☐ ☐☐☐ ☐ ☐☐☐☐

Title: _____

Goal:
The purpose is clearly and precisely stated.

Materials:
The materials or requirements are listed under appropriate headings or layout.

Method:
The steps are clear and concise.

There is a logical order to the sequence of the steps.

The steps are easy to understand and follow.

All the necessary steps are included.

Test:
An evaluation to test if the procedure has been successfully followed is included.

Writing skills:
Some instructions begin with command verbs.

The present tense is used.

Unnecessary words are omitted.

Punctuation and spelling have been checked.

Name: _____ Date: _____

Pupil **procedure** checklist

☐ ☐ ☐ ☐☐☐ ☐ ☐☐☐☐

Title: _____

Goal:
The purpose is clearly and precisely stated.

Materials:
The materials or requirements are listed under appropriate headings or layout.

Method:
The steps are clear and concise.

There is a logical order to the sequence of the steps.

The steps are easy to understand and follow.

All the necessary steps are included.

Test:
An evaluation to test if the procedure has been successfully followed is included.

Writing skills:
Some instructions begin with command verbs.

The present tense is used.

Unnecessary words are omitted.

Punctuation and spelling have been checked.

Name: _____ Date: _____

Writing format checklists

Pupil **explanation** checklist

□ □ □□□ □ □□ □ □□

Title:

Definition:

A precise statement or definition is provided.

Description:

A clear account of how and why the phenomenon occurs is included.

Information is relevant and correct.

Information is provided in a logical order.

Explanations are clearly and simply stated.

Concluding statement:

The conclusion includes an evaluation or comment.

Writing skills:

Linking words are used to show cause and effect.

The simple present tense is used.

Technical vocabulary and subject-specific terms are used.

Information is organised in paragraphs.

Spelling and punctuation have been checked.

Name: _____ Date: _____

Pupil **explanation** checklist

□ □ □□□ □ □□ □ □□

Title:

Definition:

A precise statement or definition is provided.

Description:

A clear account of how and why the phenomenon occurs is included.

Information is relevant and correct.

Information is provided in a logical order.

Explanations are clearly and simply stated.

Concluding statement:

The conclusion includes an evaluation or comment.

Writing skills:

Linking words are used to show cause and effect.

The simple present tense is used.

Technical vocabulary and subject-specific terms are used.

Information is organised in paragraphs.

Spelling and punctuation have been checked.

Name: _____ Date: _____

Writing format checklists

Pupil **discussion** checklist

☐ ☐ ☐ ☐ ☐ ☐ ☐ ☐ ☐ ☐ ☐

Title: _____

Overview:
The opening statement presents the issue and the writer's position.

Arguments:
Arguments are presented in a logical manner.
Supporting information is provided.
The strongest arguments are presented first.
The language is persuasive.

Conclusion:
A summary of the supporting arguments is given.
An evaluative comment is presented.

Writing skills:
Paragraphs state and elaborate each point.
Controlling and emotive language is used.
Different conjunctions are used.
Punctuation and spelling have been checked.

Name: _____ Date: _____

Pupil **discussion** checklist

☐ ☐ ☐ ☐ ☐ ☐ ☐ ☐ ☐ ☐ ☐

Title: _____

Overview:
The opening statement presents the issue and the writer's position.

Arguments:
Arguments are presented in a logical manner.
Supporting information is provided.
The strongest arguments are presented first.
The language is persuasive.

Conclusion:
A summary of the supporting arguments is given.
An evaluative comment is presented.

Writing skills:
Paragraphs state and elaborate each point.
Controlling and emotive language is used.
Different conjunctions are used.
Punctuation and spelling have been checked.

Name: _____ Date: _____

Blank writing format – Narrative

Title

Orientation

Who? When? Where? Why?

Complication and events

Resolution

How was it solved?

Conclusion

 Prim-Ed Publishing   www.prim-ed.com   **PRIMARY WRITING**

Blank writing format – Recount

Title

Orientation

Who? Where? When? Why?

Events

Conclusion

Blank writing format – Procedure

Title

Goal

Materials

Steps

Test

How will you know if your procedure works?

Blank writing format – Report

Title

Classification

What is it?

Description

Conclusion

What I think about it.

Prim-Ed Publishing   www.prim-ed.com

Blank writing format – Explanation

Title

Classification

What is it?

Description

Conclusion

What I think about it.

Blank writing format – Discussion

Title

Overview

What is the topic?

What is my point of view?

Arguments

Conclusion

Prim-Ed Publishing   www.prim-ed.com

Proofreading and editing checklist

Name: _____ **Date:** _____

Title: _____ **Text type:** _____

Punctuation:

I have included:

capital letters for:	
beginning sentences	☐
proper nouns..	☐
titles..	☐
question marks	☐
full stops..	☐
commas:	
in lists..	☐
for pauses	☐
to make meaning clear..	☐
apostrophes:	
for grammatical contractions..	☐
to show ownership	☐
exclamation marks	☐
quotation marks	☐
colons:	
in titles..	☐
for offset lists	☐
brackets	☐
hyphens	☐

Spelling:

I have:

checked the spelling of any unknown words..	☐
not confused words that sound the same	☐
used the correct ending for plurals..	☐

Language features:

I have included:

a variety of different verbs..	☐
correct verb tenses	☐
correct verb-subject agreement	☐
appropriate adverbs to describe verbs..	☐
suitable nouns..	☐
appropriate pronouns..	☐
interesting adjectives	☐
suitable conjunctions..	☐
a variety of prepositions	☐
paragraphing as appropriate..	☐
no double negatives..	☐

Writing:

I have read through my writing to check that:

it makes sense..	☐
it is easy to understand	☐
there are no repeated or omitted words..	☐
there are no errors of fact	☐

Class recording sheet

Date: ✓ developed • developing ✗ not yet	Pupils																							
NARRATIVES																								
Title is appropriate																								
Characters are described																								
Setting is outlined with some details																								
Complication is explained																								
Resolution is realistic and believable																								
Conclusion with character outcomes																								
RECOUNTS																								
Orientation is provided																								
Events are clearly described																								
Events are sequenced logically																								
Conclusion is relevant to context																								
PROCEDURES																								
Goal is stated																								
Material is listed																								
Steps are inclusive and sequential																								
Language is clear and concise																								
REPORTS																								
Subject is classified																								
Information is relevant and organised																								
Facts are accurate																								
A final comment is included																								
EXPLANATIONS																								
Subject is defined																								
Information is coherent and relevant																								
Vocabulary is precise																								
Information is organised logically																								
DISCUSSIONS																								
Topic and writer's position stated																								
Arguments are logical and justified																								
Language is persuasive																								
Arguments and position summarised																								
WRITING SKILLS																								
Spelling is usually correct																								
Chooses precise, appropriate vocabulary																								
Uses correct punctuation																								
Verb tense is correct and sustained																								
Ideas are relevant and organised																								
Shows sense of purpose and audience																								
Edits and proofreads writing																								

Curriculum links

Book	Year	Objectives
A	1	• write sentences by saying out loud what they are going to write about • sequence sentences to form short narratives • re-read what they have written to check that it makes sense • discuss what they have written with the teacher or other pupils • read aloud their writing clearly enough to be heard by their peers and the teacher • leave spaces between words • join words and sentences using and • begin to punctuate sentences using a capital letter and a full stop, question mark or exclamation mark • use a capital letter for the names of people, places, the days of the week and the personal pronoun 'I'
B	2	• write narratives about personal experiences and those of others (real and fictional) • write about real events • write for different purposes • plan what they are going to write about • write down ideas and/or key words, including new vocabulary • encapsulate what they want to say, sentence by sentence • evaluate their writing with the teacher and other pupils • re-read to check that their wiring makes sense and that verbs to indicate time are used correctly and consistently, including verbs in the continuous form • proof-read to check for errors in spelling, grammar and punctuation • read aloud what they have written with appropriate intonation to make the meaning clear • learn how to use both familiar and new punctuation correctly including full stops, capital letters, exclamation marks, question marks, commas for lists and apostrophes for contracted forms
C & D	3 & 4	• plan their writing by discussing writing similar to that which they are planning to write in order to understand and learn from its structure, vocabulary and grammar • discuss and record ideas • compose and rehearse sentences orally (including dialogue) • build a varied and rich vocabulary and an increasing range of sentence structures • organise paragraphs around a theme • in narratives, create settings, characters and plot • in non-narrative material, use simple organisational devices such as headings and sub-headings • evaluate and edit by assessing the effectiveness of their own and others' writing and suggesting improvements • evaluate and edit by proposing changes to grammar and vocabulary to improve consistency • proof-read for spelling and punctuation errors • read aloud their own writing, to a group or the whole class, using appropriate intonation and controlling the time and volume so that the meaning is clear
E–G	5–6	• identify the audience for and purpose of the writing, selecting the appropriate form and using often similar writing as models for their own • plan their writing by noting and developing initial ideas, drawing on reading and research where necessary • in writing narratives, considering how authors have developed characters and settings in what they have read, listened to or seen performed • select appropriate grammar and vocabulary, understanding how such choices can change and enhance meaning • in narratives, describe settings, characters and atmosphere and integrating dialogue to convey character and enhance action • use a wide range of devices to build cohesion within and across paragraphs • use further organisation and presentational devices to structure text and to guide the reader • assess the effectiveness of their own and others' writing • propose changes to vocabulary, grammar and punctuation to enhance effects and clarify meaning • ensure the consistent and correct use of tense throughout a piece of writing • ensure correct subject and verb agreement when using singular and plural, distinguishing between the language of speech and writing and choosing the appropriate register • proof-read for spelling and punctuation errors • perform their own composition, using appropriate intonation, volume, and movement so that meaning is clear

Curriculum links

Northern Ireland
Language and Literacy – Writing

Book	Year	Objectives
A	2	• observe the teacher modelling specific writing strategies • use stories as models for structuring their own writing • write in a range of genres with teacher guidance • begin to show evidence of sequence in recount and instructions
B & C	3 & 4	• participate in modelled and independent writing • talk about and plan what they are going to write • begin to check their work in relation to specific criteria • write for a variety of purposes and audiences • express thoughts and opinions in imaginative and factual writing
D–G	5–7 Extension	• participate in modelled and independent writing • discuss various features of layout in texts and apply these, as appropriate, within their own writing • write for a variety of purposes and audiences, selecting, planning and using appropriate style and form • use the skills of planning, revising and redrafting to improve their writing • express thoughts and opinions in imaginative and factual writing • begin to formulate their own personal style

Wales
English – Writing

Book	Year	Objectives
A & B	1 & 2	• organise and present imaginative and factual writing in different ways, helpful to the purpose, task and reader and incorporating some of the different characteristics of forms that are used • plan and review their writing, assembling and developing their ideas and presenting their writing clearly • write with increasing confidence, fluency and accuracy • write in a range of genres, incorporating some of the different characteristics of these forms
C–G	3–6 Extension	• use the characteristic features of literary and non-literary texts in their own writing, adapting their style to suit the audience and purpose • draft and improve their work and present writing appropriately • write for a range of purposes, for a range of real or imagined audiences, in a range of forms and in response to a range of stimuli

Curriculum links

Republic of Ireland
English Language – Writing

Book	Class	Objectives
A	Senior Infants	• receive help from the teacher, who will sometimes act as a scribe • write frequently, write for different audiences and see writing displayed • see the teacher model writing as an enjoyable experience • write about everyday experience or about something just learned • write stories
B & C	1st/2nd Class	• experience a classroom environment that encourages writing • observe the teacher as he/she models writing stories • experience how a story structure is organised by reading and listening to fiction • write regularly for different audiences, explore different genres and have writing valued • experience an abundance of oral language activity when preparing a writing task • realise that first attempts at writing are not necessarily the finished product and learn to undertake second drafts in order to improve writing • write in a variety of genres, write about something that has been learned, write the significant details about an event or an activity, write an explanation for something and write stories
D & E	3rd/4th Class	• experience a classroom environment that encourages writing • observe the teacher modelling different writing genres • use reading as a stimulus to writing • write stories that explore a variety of genres • receive and give positive responses to writing and see his/her writing valued • experience varied and consistent oral language activity as a preparation for writing • learn to use questions as a mechanism for expanding and developing a story • give sequence to ideas and events in stories • develop an appreciation of how the intended audience should influence the nature of a piece of writing • learn to revise and redraft writing • write in a variety of genres with greater sophistication • write down directions on how to perform a particular process and create stories
F & G	5th/6th Class	• experience a classroom environment that encourages writing • observe the teacher model a wide variety of writing genres • experience interesting and relevant writing challenges • receive and give constructive responses to writing and see his/her writing valued • experience a level of success in writing that will be an incentive to continue writing • experience varied and consistent oral language activity as part of the pre-writing process • observe the teacher improving writing • write independently through a process of drafting, revising, editing and publishing • choose a register of language and presentation appropriate to subject and audience • write in a variety of genres and write for a particular purpose and audience • argue the case in writing for a particular point of view • write stories

Curriculum links

Book	Level	Objectives
A–C	First	• enjoy exploring and discussing text structures • appreciate the richness of language and texts • write independently, use appropriate punctuation and order sentences in a way that makes sense • check writing makes sense throughout the writing process • present writing in a way that will make it legible and attractive for the reader • use notes and other types of writing to help create new text • consider the type of text being created and select ideas and information, organise these in a logical sequence and use interesting words • convey information, describe events or processes, share opinions and persuade the reader in different ways • explore the elements writers use in different genres and use this to compose stories with interesting structures, characters and/or settings
C–F	Second	• enjoy exploring and discussing text structures • appreciate the richness of language and texts • use appropriate punctuation, vary sentence structures and divide work into paragraphs • check writing makes sense and meets its purpose throughout the writing process • consider the impact that layout and presentation have • use notes and other types of writing to create new text • consider the type of text being created and select ideas and information, organise these in an appropriate way for the purpose and use suitable vocabulary for the audience • use language and style to engage and/or influence the reader • convey information, describe events and explain processes in different ways • persuade, argue, explore issues or express an opinion using relevant supporting detail and/or evidence • write for different purposes and readers • explore the elements writers use in different genres and use this to compose stories with an interesting and appropriate structure, interesting characters and/or settings which come to life
F–G	Third	• enjoy exploring and discussing increasingly complex texts and structures • appreciate the influence texts can have • punctuate and structure different types of sentences and arrange these into paragraphs • review and edit writing to ensure it meets its purpose and communicates meaning throughout the writing process • consider the impact that layout and presentation will have on the reader • use notes and other types of writing to create original text • consider the type of text being created and select ideas and information, organise these in an appropriate way for the purpose and use suitable vocabulary for the audience • engage and/or influence readers through use of language, style and tone as appropriate to the genre • convey information, describe events and explain processes or concepts • persuade, argue, evaluate, explore issues or express an opinion, using a clear line of thought and relevant supporting detail and/or evidence • explore the elements writers use and compose texts in different genres, using some of the conventions of chosen genre successfully and/or creating convincing narratives, characters and settings

Structural and language features are shown on the left and right of the text below.

Title	Tamar and Cuza, the priest
Orientation – who, when and where	In 700 AD in the city of Cobar **Lived** a Mayan man whose name was Tamar. He was very wealthy, a noble by birth, A descendant of the Hero Twins, and wide of girth.
Complication involving the main character) **and events** are described in chronological order	A proud and selfish man was he Who **cared** for nothing except what others would see. He pierced his ears and tattooed his skin. He wore his black hair as straight as a pin. He wore tall hats and embroidered clothes, (An important man should have baubles and bows!) He bathed every day and filled up his house With mirrors to reflect his haughty countenance. Whenever he walked down the crowded streets, A slave would hide his face from all he would meet. He spent his days in leisure and sloth. He only stirred himself to adjust his hair cloth. One day a priest named Cuza passed by. He nodded a greeting but Tamar avoided his eye. 'I'm better than he. I rule the town. He is only a priest. Just look at his gown!' Cuza was insulted by this very **haughty** act. He decided to retaliate, so planned his attack. He sent a message to Tamar the next day Inviting him to a ceremony where he could pray. As soon as Tamar arrived that day, Cuza handed him a prayer to say. Tamar started to proclaim to the people there And with his first words triggered Cuza's **snare**.
Resolution to the complication	No sooner had the words been said When Tamar was as good as dead. On the ground, where he had prayed Was now a figure made from clay. It rattled and showed its fine, bright clothes **But** no-one could object to those. From that day on, in every rite A pottery figure was always in sight.
Conclusion – showing what has changed and what the character has learnt	**Because** Tamar showed that he was proud, Selfish, rude and often loud, Thanks to him to this very day We can learn about life — the Mayan way.

- verbs in the past tense; e.g. **Lived**, **cared**

- appropriate paragraphing

- descriptive language; e.g. **haughty**, **snare**

- conjunctions to connect ideas; e.g. **But**, **Because**

Answers

Page 4

1–2. Teacher check

3. (a) Tamar was rude, foolish and proud.

   (b) Answers will vary but will include: He pierced his ears and tattooed his skin; He wore his black hair as straight as a pin; He wore tall hats and embroidered his clothes; He bathed every day; He looked at himself in the mirror every day; Slaves had to hold a cloth in front of his face when he walked down the street as he considered other people weren't good enough to look at him.

   (c) Pupils should have drawn a picture of Tamar walking down the street, refusing to greet the priest.

4. (a) Cuza got Tamar to say 'magic' words in a prayer which turned him into a pottery figure.

   (b) Teacher check

5. Answers could include: The Mayans made little pottery figures and used them in religious ceremonies. Some rattled or whistled. They were small but were detailed and painted very brightly. Figures which have been discovered include a man with a beard on a throne, a person in a wide hat, a ballplayer wearing padded clothing and a musician shaking a rattle.

Teacher information

- This narrative is written in poetry form and is based on information about aspects of the Mayan way of life. The Mayans had a very distinct class system. Nobles and priests were at the top of the class system. Nobles spent a lot of time on their appearance.
- The complication for this narrative doesn't appear until a lot of background information is given about the main character, Tamar, and is found further down in the narrative.
- Ask pupils to predict what the narrative could be about before reading the poem. The names of the characters may give some indication.
- Pupils read the narrative.
- Discuss the title and its suitability, the information which needs to be included in an orientation, the complication or problem and how it was resolved. Finally, decide whether the ending is a good one or whether it could be improved. Discuss the language features included in a narrative, including paragraphs to introduce new ideas, descriptive

language, conjunctions to connect ideas, and verbs in the past tense. Ask pupils to find examples of each in the text.
- Pupils complete the analysis on page 4.
- Before pupils attempt to use the narrative plan on page 5 to plan their story about a person living in an ancient civilisation, model the process of planning then writing one for them. NOTE: Pupils will need some background knowledge of the time they are writing about before commencing their narrative.
- Pupils need to understand that the plan is for ideas and that they will write their actual story later.
- A narrative based on a person living in an ancient civilisation can be used to demonstrate pupils' understanding of a particular time frame within the context of a history unit. (Context)
- Pupils can publish their narratives using an appropriate font on the computer, print them and glue them onto an 'ancient manuscript' for display or to share with another class. (Display/Publishing/Audience)

TAMAR AND CUZA, THE PRIEST

In 700 AD in the city of Cobar
Lived a Mayan man whose name was Tamar.
He was very wealthy, a noble by birth,
A descendant of the Hero Twins, and wide of girth.

A proud and selfish man was he
Who cared for nothing except what others would see.
He pierced his ears and tattooed his skin.
He wore his black hair as straight as a pin.

He wore tall hats and embroidered clothes.
(An important man should have baubles and bows!)
He bathed every day and filled up his house
With mirrors to reflect his haughty countenance.

Whenever he walked down the crowded streets,
A slave would hide his face from all he would meet.
He spent his days in leisure and sloth.
He only stirred himself to adjust his hair cloth.

One day a priest named Cuza passed by.
He nodded a greeting but Tamar avoided his eye.
'I'm better than he. I rule the town.
He is only a priest. Just look at his gown!'

Cuza was insulted by this very haughty act.
He decided to retaliate, so planned his attack.
He sent a message to Tamar the next day
Inviting him to a ceremony where he could pray.

As soon as Tamar arrived that day,
Cuza handed him a prayer to say.
Tamar started to proclaim to the people there
And with his first words triggered Cuza's snare.

No sooner had the words been said
Proud Tamar was as good as dead.
On the ground, where he had prayed
Was now a figure made from clay.

It rattled and showed its fine, bright clothes
But no-one could object to those.
From that day on, in every rite
A pottery figure was always in sight.

Because Tamar showed that he was proud,
Selfish, rude and often loud,
Thanks to him to this very day
We can learn about life — the Mayan way.

Use the narrative on page 3 to complete the page.

1. Title

Write an alternative title.

2. Orientation

Rewrite the first verse (which forms the orientation) as one concise sentence which includes all the necessary information.

_____

_____

3. Complication and events

(a) What was the complication?

_____

_____

_____

(b) List some things that Tamar did which tell you that he only cared about his appearance.

(c) One event occurred to make someone decide to teach Tamar a lesson. Draw a picture of that event.

4. Resolution

(a) How did Cuza solve his problem?

_____

_____

_____

_____

_____

(b) Write an alternative solution to the problem.

_____

_____

_____

_____

_____

5. Conclusion

Research a fact about the small pottery figures the Mayans made.

_____

_____

_____

_____

_____

_____

_____

1. Plan a narrative about a person living in an ancient civilisation.

Title

Orientation

Complication and events

Resolution

Conclusion

2. Write your narrative. If you choose, it may be written as a poem.

3. Edit your work.

Structural and language features are shown on the left and right of the text below.

Title	**The legend of the golden snail**	
Orientation – who, when and where	A long time ago in Indonesia, there **lived** a prince called Raden who was married to a princess named Dewi. They lived in an **ornate** palace with many beautiful flowers in the gardens.	• verbs in the past tense; e.g. **lived**, **saw**
Complication involving the main character) **and events** are described in chronological order	One day, while Dewi was walking in the palace gardens, she **saw** a snail among her flowers. She asked one of her servants to pick it up and throw it away. The snail was really an old witch who had disguised herself. The witch became very angry with Dewi **so** she put a curse on her and turned her into a golden snail. Then she threw the snail into the river, which carried her away from the palace and into the forest.	• conjunctions to connect ideas; **so**, **and**
	In the forest lived a poor widow who made her living catching fish. On this day, she had been trying unsuccessfully to catch fish in her net. Finally, she pulled her net out of the water to go home. There, in the bottom of her net, she saw a snail with a shell that shone like gold. She took it home **and** placed it in a clay pot.	• appropriate paragraphing
	The next morning when she woke, she found her floor had been swept and a meal had been placed on the table. This happened for many days, until she decided to find out who was helping her.	• descriptive language; e.g. **ornate, holy**
	One day, she pretended to go out, but returned quietly and hid. Soon, she saw the snail crawl out of the pot. A lovely young woman emerged from the shell. She then cleaned the house and cooked a meal. At once, the old woman realised that the young woman was under a spell and she was determined to break the curse. She seized the empty shell and quickly threw it into the river. The young woman told her story to the old woman and continued to live with her.	
	Some years passed. The king persuaded Prince Raden he needed to find a new wife. Raden was determined not to marry anyone unless she looked exactly like his former wife. So he travelled from town to town with his faithful servant searching for a new wife.	
	One day, Prince Raden and his servant came upon the hut near the river. They asked the old woman for food and drink. After eating and enjoying his meal, Raden wished to thank the person who had prepared it. The old woman brought out her 'daughter', who was really princess Dewi.	
Resolution – to the complication	As soon as he saw her, Prince Raden knew that she was the bride he wanted. Dewi refused to marry him until he went to heaven and collected the **holy** gamelan, a special Javanese orchestra which made music without having to be touched. Raden agreed. For one hundred days, he fasted and meditated in the forest until finally the gods decided to grant his wish. On their wedding day, the holy gamelan played its beautiful music and Dewi was able to tell her husband the story of the witch's curse and the golden snail.	
Conclusion – showing what has changed and what the character has learnt	The old woman lived happily ever after in the palace with them and had everything she could possibly want.	

Teacher information

• In Jakarta, this legend is perpetuated by a huge theatre in golden colours which looks like a large snail. Called Keong Emas (the Golden Snail), the theatre has a circular three-dimensional screen, reported to be one of the largest of its type in the world.

• Pupils read the narrative.

• Discuss the title and its suitability, the information which needs to be included in an orientation, the complication or problem and how it was resolved. Finally decide whether the ending is a good one or whether it could be improved.

• Pupils may offer other suggestions for suitable endings. Discuss the language features included in a narrative, including paragraphs to introduce new ideas, descriptive language, conjunctions to connect ideas and verbs in the past tense. Ask pupils to find examples of each in the text.

• Allow pupils to complete the analysis on page 8.

• Model the process of planning then writing a narrative based upon a familiar legend or folktale. Pupils may wish to offer suggestions for a suitable legend to plan and write about.

• Before pupils attempt to use the narrative plan on page 9,

discuss some suggestions and allow time for research.

• Pupils need to understand that the plan is for ideas only and that they will write their real story later.

• Pupils may write their plan in bullet points.

• Pupil narratives can be compiled, illustrated and published in a book to be presented to the teacher of a younger class for reading. (Publishing/Audience)

• Pupils may retell legends or folktales as narratives when completing a unit about a particular country. (Context)

• Pupils may display their narrative with a large pictorial representation in watercolours or pastel paints. (Display))

Answers

Page 8

1–2. Teacher check

3. (a) Dewi was turned into a golden snail.

(b) – (c) Teacher check

4–5. Teacher check

The legend of the golden snail

A long time ago in Indonesia, there lived a prince called Raden who was married to a princess named Dewi. They lived in an ornate palace with many beautiful flowers in the gardens.

One day, while Dewi was walking in the palace gardens, she saw a snail among her flowers. She asked one of her servants to pick it up and throw it away. The snail was really an old witch who had disguised herself. The witch became very angry with Dewi so she put a curse on her and turned her into a golden snail. Then she threw the snail into the river, which carried her away from the palace and into the forest.

In the forest lived a poor widow who made her living catching fish. On this day, she had been trying unsuccessfully to catch fish in her net. Finally, she pulled her net out of the water to go home. There, in the bottom of her net, she saw a snail with a shell that shone like gold. She took it home and placed it in a clay pot.

The next morning when she woke, she found her floor had been swept and a meal had been placed on the table. This happened for many days, until she decided to find out who was helping her.

One day, she pretended to go out, but returned quietly and hid. Soon, she saw the snail crawl out of the pot. A lovely young woman emerged from the shell. She then cleaned the house and cooked a meal. At once, the old woman realised that the young woman was under a spell and she was determined to break the curse. She seized the empty shell and quickly threw it into the river. The young woman told her story to the old woman and continued to live with her.

Some years passed. The king persuaded Prince Raden he needed to find a new wife. Raden was

determined not to marry anyone unless she looked exactly like his former wife. So he travelled from town to town with his faithful servant searching for a new wife.

One day, Prince Raden and his servant came upon the hut near the river. They asked the old woman for food and drink. After eating and enjoying his meal, Raden wished to thank the person who had prepared it. The old woman brought out her 'daughter', who was really princess Dewi.

As soon as he saw her, Prince Raden knew that she was the bride he wanted. Dewi refused to marry him until he went to heaven and collected the holy gamelan, a special Javanese instrument which made music without having to be touched. Raden agreed. For one hundred days, he fasted and meditated in the forest until finally the gods decided to grant his wish. On their wedding day, the holy gamelan played its beautiful music and Dewi was able to tell her husband the story of the witch's curse and the golden snail.

The old woman lived happily ever after in the palace with them and had everything she could possibly want.

Use the narrative on page 7 to complete the page.

1. Title

The title of a narrative is very important. It must be appropriate and interesting.

Is the title of this narrative appropriate and interesting?   **yes** ☐ **no** ☐

Explain.

_____

_____

_____

2. Orientation

(a) Tick the boxes.

   (i) The characters are introduced. ☐

   (ii) The characters are described. ☐

   (iii) Information about where the story happened is provided. ☐

   (iv) The time the narrative took place is stated. ☐

3. Complication and events

(a) What was the complication? _____

_____

(b) Use the boxes to draw illustrations of two important events.

(c) Rewrite the following sentence, adding more descriptive language.

'A lovely young woman emerged from the shell.'

_____

_____

4. Resolution

(a) Was the resolution logical and believable?

  yes ☐   **no** ☐

  Explain. _____

  _____

  _____

(b) Discuss other possible resolutions with a partner.

5. Conclusion

Write an alternate phrase for 'lived happily ever after' for the ending.

_____

_____

_____

_____

1. Plan a narrative in the form of a legend. You may like to research legends for ideas.

Title

Orientation

Complication and events

Resolution

Conclusion

2. Write your narrative.

3. Edit your work.

Structural and language features are shown on the left and right of the text below.

	Friends are where you find them	
Title		
Orientation – who, when, where, what	Not long ago, on a dark, wet night, deep in the rainforest of South America, a solitary toucan **named** Clyde **sat** precariously on the branch of a tree. This evening, he had awoken to find his small family had flown away and left him alone on the branch. He was not a good flyer so he knew he would not be able to catch them. He decided to wait on the branch until they returned.	• verbs in the past tense; e.g. **sat**, **named**
Complication involving the main character) **and events** are described in chronological order	Presently, he heard eerie rustling in the leaves of the branch next to him. The night was so black that he could not see very far, **so** he croaked into the darkness, 'Who's there?' 'It is only me!' replied a voice. Clyde didn't think that the voice sounded very menacing, **but** to make certain the speaker was a friend and not an enemy, he decided to subtly extract some information. 'I was left behind when my family flew away', croaked Clyde. 'I'm afraid I'm not a good flyer.' 'Neither am I', came a quiet reply. 'I would rather spend my time in the trees than on the ground.' 'Good!' thought Clyde. 'At least the voice doesn't belong to an eagle!' 'It's lucky that I found some tasty insects not far from the tree,' added Clyde, 'otherwise, I would be feeling very empty right now!' 'Yes', answered the voice in a satisfied tone.' You must have discovered the same nest that I did! Very tasty indeed!' 'Better and better', thought Clyde. 'This is an animal who doesn't fly well, like me! It likes being in the trees, also like me AND it likes to eat insects, just like me! It must be another toucan! But just to be certain, I'll need one more piece of information!' Because he felt safe surrounded by the black night and no-one could witness his embarrassment, he offered his most private thoughts. 'I'm very glad, at times like this, that my nose is as big as it is. It's helped me find my food and to sniff out another toucan to be my friend during the long, dark night!' confessed Clyde. The sound of the wind shifting the leaves was heard and the drip of rain seemed to **echo like a drum**, but no noise came from the voice. Clyde realised that he had made a terrible mistake. He waited for **fierce** jaws to seize him and end his life. Rustling came from the leaves as he heard something approach. He squeezed his eyes tightly together—not daring to look. He waited and waited but nothing happened. Gradually, he opened his eyes until he could see a long face staring at him.	• conjunctions to connect ideas; **so**, **but** • appropriate paragraphing • descriptive language; e.g. **echo like a drum**, **fierce**
Resolution – to the complication	'I know exactly how you feel', the voice said. 'My snout is long as well, but my tongue is even worse! It's lucky that I prefer to be on my own! My name is Bonnie and I'm pleased to meet you!'	
Conclusion – showing what has changed and what the character has learnt	Clyde, the toucan, and Bonnie, the anteater, were friends from that day on. After all, they had quite a lot in common!	

Teacher information

- Pupils read the narrative.
- Discuss the title and its suitability, the information which needs to be included in an orientation, the complication or problem and how it was resolved. Finally decide whether the ending is a good one or whether it could be improved.
- Pupils may offer other suggestions for suitable endings. Discuss the language features included in a narrative, including paragraphs to introduce new ideas, descriptive language, conjunctions to connect ideas, and verbs in the past tense. Ask pupils to find examples of each in the text.
- Allow pupils to complete the analysis on page 12.
- Model the process of planning then writing a narrative based upon two animals from a particular environment such as a desert. Pupils may wish to offer suggestions.
- Before pupils attempt to use the narrative plan on page 9, discuss some suggestions. Pupils should, if possible, try to include background information about the animals in their narrative and may need time for research.
- Pupils need to understand that the plan is for ideas only and that they will write their real story later.
- Pupils may write their plan in bullet points.

- Pupil narratives can be compiled, illustrated and published as a storybook for younger children. (Publishing/Audience)
- Pupils can write narratives when completing a unit about a particular biome, ecosystem or environment. (Context)
- Pupils can display their narrative with a cartoon representation. (Display)

Answers

Page 12

1. Teacher check
2. (a) who: a solitary toucan; when: not long ago, on a dark wet, night; where: deep in the rainforest of South America
   (b) Teacher check
3. (a) … that Clyde wanted a friend to stay with him during the night
   (b) Teacher check
   (c) The two animals reveal themselves.
4–5. Teacher check

Friends are where you find them

Not long ago, on a dark, wet night, deep in the rainforest of South America, a solitary toucan named Clyde sat precariously on the branch of a tree.

This evening, he had awoken to find his small family had flown away and left him alone on the branch. He was not a good flyer so he knew he would not be able to catch them. He decided to wait on the branch until they returned.

Presently, he heard eerie rustling in the leaves of the branch next to him. The night was so black that he could not see very far, so he croaked into the darkness, 'Who's there?'

'It is only me!' replied a voice.

Clyde didn't think that the voice sounded very menacing, but to make certain the speaker was a friend and not an enemy, he decided to subtly extract some information.

'I was left behind when my family flew away', croaked Clyde. 'I'm afraid I'm not a good flyer.'

'Neither am I', came a quiet reply. 'I would rather spend my time in the trees than on the ground.'

'Good!' thought Clyde. 'At least the voice doesn't belong to an eagle!'

'It's lucky that I found some tasty insects not far from the tree,' added Clyde, 'otherwise, I would be feeling very empty right now!'

'Yes', answered the voice in a satisfied tone. 'You must have discovered the same nest that I did! Very tasty indeed!'

'Better and better', thought Clyde. 'This is an animal who doesn't fly well, like me! It likes being in the trees, also like me AND it likes to eat insects, just like me! It must be another toucan! But just to be certain, I'll need one more piece of information!'

Because he felt safe surrounded by the black night and no-one could witness his embarrassment, he offered his most private thoughts.

'I'm very glad, at times like this, that my nose is as big as it is. It's helped me find my food and to sniff out another toucan to be my friend during the long, dark night!' confessed Clyde.

The sound of the wind shifting the leaves was heard and the drip of rain seemed to echo like a drum, but no noise came from the voice. Clyde realised that he had made a terrible mistake. He waited for fierce jaws to seize him and end his life. Rustling came from the leaves as he heard something approach. He squeezed his eyes tightly together—not daring to look. He waited and waited but nothing happened. Gradually, he opened his eyes until he could see a long face staring at him.

'I know exactly how you feel', the voice said. 'My snout is long as well, but my tongue is even worse! It's lucky that I prefer to be on my own! My name is Bonnie and I'm pleased to meet you!'

Clyde, the toucan, and Bonnie, the anteater, were friends from that day on. After all, they had quite a lot in common!

Use the narrative on page 11 to complete the page.

1. Title

Write a new title for the narrative.

2. Orientation

(a) Write words and phrases from the orientation to complete the boxes.

> **who?**

> **when?**

> **where?**

(b) Rewrite the first sentence (p. 11) by substituting words with a similar meaning to the words and phrases in the boxes above.

3. Complication and events

(a) The complication was

_____

_____

_____

_____

This narrative places a lot of importance on conversation, particularly Bonnie's replies to Clyde's questions.

(b) Explain why this has been done.

_____

_____

_____

_____

(c) What happens at the end of the conversation of the two main characters?

4. Resolution

(a) Was the resolution a good one?   yes ☐ no ☐

Give reasons for your answer.

_____

_____

(b) Briefly write an alternative resolution.

_____

_____

5. Conclusion

Write a new sentence to end the narrative.

1. Plan a narrative about two animals from the same environment, ecosystem or biome.

Title

Orientation

Complication and events

Resolution

Conclusion

2. Write your narrative.

3. Edit your work.

Structural and language features are shown on the left and right of the text below.

Title	**The eruption of Mount Vesuvius**
Orientation – who, when, where, why	**On the morning of** 24 August, 79 AD, Mount Vesuvius in southern Italy began to erupt. Despite a number of geological warnings, the eruption took the population of the nearby towns of Pompeii and Herculaneum by complete surprise. In the days preceding the eruption, there had been a number of earth tremors but these were ignored by the population as seismic activity was not unusual in the region.
Events – in order with detail	**On the fateful day**, the peak of the volcano was completely blown off as a large column of smoke exploded from its centre. It spread high into the sky like a giant tree, its branches covering the land with blankets of dense, choking ash. The strong coastal winds blew the burning clouds over a wide area, **obliterating** the sun and turning day into night. Fires burned in the bay as glowing pumice landed on ships' sails, quickly setting them alight. The sea breezes fanned the flames which easily spread to the wooden masts and hulls. On land, pockets of fire added another hazard to the already perilous situation.
	The people of the towns were hysterical with panic. Should they shelter indoors from the falling ash and volcanic rock or remain outside, as their homes collapsed? The commotion was deafening; from the roar of volcanic activity and the crumbling of buildings to the screams of terror from people fleeing for their lives and searching for loved ones. Thousands of people were trying to leave the towns, hoping to outrun the volcanic rain, but their escape was hampered by fallen debris and the panicking crowds. Fresh air had been sucked away, replaced by a foul-smelling gas. Drinking water was contaminated, leaving no means of relief from the suffocating effects of the fallout.
	After hours of terror which many believed signalled the end of the world, the first pyroclastic surges began. The avalanche of white-hot ash, pumice and molten lava hugged the land as it raced down the volcano at 100 km/h. The intense heat of the first surge hit Herculaneum, taking the last breaths from sheltering refugees before engulfing them in volcanic graves. Further surges reached Pompeii, burying the city and hiding the devastation and carnage.
	On the coastline, a drawback of the sea left fish beached on the sand before the first wave of the tsunami hit. The waters of the Mediterranean, racing over the burning land, sent clouds of water vapour hissing into the air. The atmosphere was filled with a combination of steam, ash and the stench of sulphur.
	After 24 hours of raging anger, Vesuvius's energy **was spent**. The volcano **calmed**, but in the wake of its fury lay the complete destruction of a once rich and vibrant commercial region.
Conclusion – indicating value of event	For more than 1500 years, the cities lay undiscovered until some artefacts were found which raised an interest in the area. But it wasn't until the mid-nineteenth century that archaeological excavations began. These uncovered information about how the people of Pompeii and Herculaneum lived and the awful way in which so many died.

- appropriate paragraphing

- varied and interesting vocabulary; e.g. **On the fateful day**, **obliterating**

- vocabulary to suggest passing of time; e.g. **On the morning of**, **After hours**

- verbs in the past tense; **was spent**, **calmed**

Teacher information

- Discuss that a recount may come in many forms; e.g. diary entry, newspaper report, eyewitness account.
- Read and discuss the recount on page 15 with the pupils.
- Discuss the different sections of the framework and ensure pupils understand how the text fits into each.
- Emphasise the language features listed to the right of the text above.
- Work through the analysis on page 16 with the pupils.
- Plan a similar recount, writing ideas for each section within the framework and discuss and model how the plan is transformed into a coherent piece of text.
- Pupils use page 17 to plan and then write a recount about a natural disaster.
- Pupils could choose a disaster based on a topic being studied in geography. (Context)
- Pupils display their work around a time line to indicate when the events occurred. (Display)
- Pupils display pictures and headlines of disasters around a world map to indicate where the events occurred. (Display)
- Pupils present work in chronological order in a book as a resource for other classes. (Publishing/Purpose/Audience)

Answers

Page 16
1. Teacher check
2. name: Vesuvius
   location: southern Italy
   date of eruption: 24 August, 79 AD
   cities affected: Pompeii and Herculaneum
3. (a) earth tremors – previous day
   peak blown off – morning
   column of smoke exploding from centre – morning
   pyroclastic surges – after many hours
   (b) Teacher check
4. The excavations uncovered information about the destruction caused by the eruption of Mount Vesuvius and how the people of that time had lived.

The eruption of Mount Vesuvius

On the morning of 24 August, 79 AD, Mount Vesuvius in southern Italy began to erupt. Despite a number of geological warnings, the eruption took the population of the nearby towns of Pompeii and Herculaneum by complete surprise. In the days preceding the eruption, there had been a number of earth tremors but these were ignored by the population as seismic activity was not unusual in the region.

On the fateful day, the peak of the volcano was completely blown off as a large column of smoke exploded from its centre. It spread high into the sky like a giant tree, its branches covering the land with blankets of dense, choking ash. The strong coastal winds blew the burning clouds over a wide area, obliterating the sun and turning day into night. Fires burned in the bay as glowing pumice landed on ships' sails, quickly setting them alight. The sea breezes fanned the flames which easily spread to the wooden masts and hulls. On land, pockets of fire added another hazard to the already perilous situation.

The people of the towns were hysterical with panic. Should they shelter indoors from the falling ash and volcanic rock or remain outside, as their homes collapsed? The commotion was deafening; from the roar of volcanic activity and the crumbling of buildings to the screams of terror from people fleeing for their lives and searching for loved ones. Thousands of people were trying to leave the towns, hoping to outrun the volcanic rain, but their escape was hampered by fallen debris and the panicking crowds. Fresh air had been sucked away,

replaced by a foul-smelling gas. Drinking water was contaminated, leaving no means of relief from the suffocating effects of the fallout.

After hours of terror which many believed signalled the end of the world, the first pyroclastic surges began. The avalanche of white-hot ash, pumice and molten lava hugged the land as it raced down the volcano at 100 km/h. The intense heat of the first surge hit Herculaneum, taking the last breaths from sheltering refugees before engulfing them in volcanic graves. Further surges reached Pompeii, burying the city and hiding the devastation and carnage.

On the coastline, a drawback of the sea left fish beached on the sand before the first wave of the tsunami hit. The waters of the Mediterranean, racing over the burning land, sent clouds of water vapour hissing into the air. The atmosphere was filled with a combination of steam, ash and the stench of sulphur.

After 24 hours of raging anger, Vesuvius's energy was spent. The volcano calmed, but in the wake of its fury lay the complete destruction of a once rich and vibrant commercial region.

For more than 1500 years, the cities lay undiscovered until some artefacts were found which raised an interest in the area. But it wasn't until the mid-nineteenth century that archaeological excavations began. These uncovered information about how the people of Pompeii and Herculaneum lived and the awful way in which so many died.

Use the recount on page 15 to complete the page.

1. Title

(a) Write a selection of adjectives and phrases to describe the eruption of and the devastation caused by Mount Vesuvius.

(b) Use your ideas to write an interesting title for the recount.

_____

2. Orientation

Complete the fact file for the volcano.

Name: _____

Location:

_____

_____

Date of eruption:

_____

Cities affected:

_____

_____

3. Events

(a) Write the four stages of Vesuvius's eruption, stating when each event occurred.

Stage 1:	Stage 2:	Stage 3:	Stage 4:

(b) Are the effects of the eruption described in the order in which they occurred?   yes ☐ no ☐

Explain why you think the writer has done this.

_____

_____

_____

4. Conclusion

Why were the archaeological excavations begun in the mid-nineteenth century so important?

_____

_____

1. Plan a recount of a natural disaster.

Title

Orientation

Events

Conclusion

2. Write your recount.

3. Edit your work.

Structural and language features are shown on the left and right of the text below.

Title	**Olympic Games opening ceremony – Sydney 2000**

• appropriate paragraphing

Orientation – who, when, where, why	At sunset on 15 September 2000, the long awaited games of the 27th Olympiad were opened at the Homebush Stadium in Sydney. To mark the beginning of a two-week festival of international sport, 100 000 spectators were treated to a spectacular pageant of Australian culture and Olympic traditions.

• varied and interesting vocabulary; e.g. **dramatic tapestry**, **depicting**

Events – in order with detail	An Aussie welcome began the ceremony, as a lone rider on a chestnut stallion charged into the stadium to the theme of *Man from Snowy River*. As he came to a halt and cracked his stockwhip, he was joined by 120 men and women galloping towards him on horseback. A huge banner bearing the familiar phrase 'G'day' welcomed the crowd in classic Australian style. A **dramatic tapestry** of Australia's natural and social history then unfolded.

• vocabulary to suggest passing of time; e.g. **At the end of**, **As the evening continued**

Seven segments, **depicting** the environment, history and culture of Australia, were cleverly blended into one as Hero Girl, played by Nikki Webster, was taken by the Aboriginal Songman, Djakapurra Munyarryun, on a journey of exploration. **At the end of** the spectacular performance, Hero Girl and Songman rose high above the stadium as the other performers said their farewell.

As the evening continued, the Sydney 2000 Olympic Band preceded the parade of athletes and officials from 199 countries. In keeping with tradition, the Greek team was the first to step into the arena. As the Australian team appeared, the roar from the capacity crowd was tumultuous. Spectators stood and waved their flags, cheering on the home team.

• verbs in the past tense; **was**, **were spoken**

Next came the welcoming speech by Juan Antonio Samaranch, President of the International Olympic Committee. This was followed by Sir William Deane, declaring the Games of the XXVII Olympiad, open. At his final words, a giant silk Olympic flag was carried into the stadium by eight Australian Olympians. The flag was fed down to the arena, covering the assembled athletes and officials.

The declaration of oaths which has been part of the Olympic programme since the Antwerp Games in 1920, **was** next on the agenda. These **were spoken** by Rachelle Hawes, captain of the Australian women's hockey team who took the athletes' oath and by Peter Kerr, the Australian water polo official who took the oath of impartiality on behalf of all judges and officials.

The grand finale of the evening was the entry of the Olympic flame, the last stage of a relay which had lasted six months and covered five continents. As Tina Arena sang 'The flame', the torch was carried by six of Australia's greatest female athletes to commemorate one hundred years of women's participation in the Games. Dressed in a dazzling white outfit, Cathy Freeman took the torch and lit the Olympic cauldron, which was then raised to the top of the Olympic stadium where it would remain for the duration of the Games.

Conclusion – indicating value of event	The opening ceremony of Sydney 2000 was watched on television by millions throughout the world. Viewers enjoyed the dramatic celebration of the Australian nation and the established traditions of the modern Olympic era. As an introduction to each Games, the opening ceremony will always be a premier event.

Teacher information

- Discuss that a recount may come in many forms; e.g. diary entry, newspaper report, eyewitness account.
- Read and discuss the recount on page 19 with the pupils.
- Discuss the different sections of the framework and ensure pupils understand how the text fits into each.
- Emphasise the writing skills listed to the right of the text above.
- Work through the analysis on page 20 with the pupils.
- Plan a similar recount, writing ideas for each section within the framework and discuss and model how the plan is transformed into a coherent piece of text.
- Pupils use page 21 to plan and then write a recount about a special event.
- Pupils could choose a subject based on a topic being studied in history or geography. (Context)
- Small groups of pupils could research different events and present factual information to the rest of the class and/or other classes before reading individual recounts. (Audience/ Purpose)

- Recounts could be categorised and presented as a book to be used as a resource by others. (Publishing/Audience/ Purpose)
- A montage of photographs and pictures could be made to highlight a display of pupils' work. (Publishing/Display)

Answers

Page 20
1. Teacher check
2. Teacher check
3. (a) an Aussie welcome with men and women on horseback
   (b) the journey of exploration with Hero Girl and the Aboriginal Songman
   (c) the parade of athletes
   (d) the welcoming speech and the unfurling of the Olympic flag
   (e) the declaration of oaths
   (f) the lighting of the Olympic cauldron
4. (a) a colourful public performance or display
   (b) very noisy, loud cheering
   (c) not taking sides,
5. Teacher check

Olympic Games opening ceremony – Sydney 2000

At sunset on 15 September 2000, the long awaited games of the 27th Olympiad were opened at the Homebush Stadium in Sydney. To mark the beginning of a two-week festival of international sport, 100 000 spectators were treated to a spectacular pageant of Australian culture and Olympic traditions.

An Aussie welcome began the ceremony, as a lone rider on a chestnut stallion charged into the stadium to the theme of *Man from Snowy River*. As he came to a halt and cracked his stockwhip, he was joined by 120 men and women galloping towards him on horseback. A huge banner bearing the familiar phrase 'G'day' welcomed the crowd in classic Australian style. A dramatic tapestry of Australia's natural and social history then unfolded.

Seven segments, depicting the environment, history and culture of Australia, were cleverly blended into one as Hero Girl, played by Nikki Webster, was taken by the Aboriginal Songman, Djakapurra Munyarryun, on a journey of exploration. At the end of the spectacular performance, Hero Girl and Songman rose high above the stadium as the other performers said their farewell.

As the evening continued, the Sydney 2000 Olympic Band preceded the parade of athletes and officials from 199 countries. In keeping with tradition, the Greek team was the first to step into the arena. As the Australian team appeared, the roar from the capacity crowd was tumultuous. Spectators stood and waved their flags, cheering on the home team.

Next came the welcoming speech by Juan Antonio Samaranch, President of the International Olympic Committee. This was followed by Sir William Deane, declaring the Games of the XXVII Olympiad, open. At his final words, a giant silk Olympic flag was carried into the stadium by eight Australian Olympians. The flag was fed down to the arena, covering the assembled athletes and officials.

The declaration of oaths which has been part of the Olympic programme since the Antwerp Games in 1920, was next on the agenda. These were spoken by Rachelle Hawes, captain of the Australian women's hockey team who took the athletes' oath and by Peter Kerr, the Australian water polo official who took the oath of impartiality on behalf of all judges and officials.

The grand finale of the evening was the entry of the Olympic flame, the last stage of a relay which had lasted five months and covered six continents. As Tina Arena sang 'The flame', the torch was carried by six of Australia's greatest female athletes to commemorate one hundred years of women's participation in the Games. Dressed in a dazzling white outfit, Cathy Freeman took the torch and lit the Olympic cauldron, which was then raised to the top of the Olympic stadium where it would remain for the duration of the Games.

The opening ceremony of Sydney 2000 was watched on television by millions throughout the world. Viewers enjoyed the dramatic celebration of the Australian nation and the established traditions of the modern Olympic era. As an introduction to each Games, the opening ceremony will always be a premier event.

Use the recount on page 19 to complete the page.

1. Title

Write a more imaginative title for this recount.

2. Orientation

Write another paragraph for the orientation, answering the questions:
Who? When? and Where?

3. Events

(a) Briefly describe each of the six key events.

(i) _____

(ii) _____

(iii) _____

(iv) _____

(v) _____

(vi) _____

Descriptive language improves the quality of a piece of writing.

(b) Write definitions for these words.

(i) pageant	(ii) tumultuous	(iii) impartial

4. Conclusion

Imagine you were present at the Sydney 2000 opening ceremony. Write a concluding paragraph for this recount, including a personal comment.

_____

_____

_____

_____

1. Plan a recount of a special event.

Title

Orientation

Events

Conclusion

2. Write your recount.

3. Edit your work.

Structural and language features are shown on the left and right of the text below.

Title	Space race

Orientation –
who, when, where, why

On Wednesday 16 July 1969, the space rocket *Apollo 11* stood on the NASA launch pad at the Kennedy Space Centre in Florida. It was hoped that its success would crown the USA as leaders in the space race, ahead of the USSR. Seven months earlier, Neil Armstrong, Edwin Buzz Aldrin and Michael Collins had been named as the astronauts to man the craft on its historic voyage.

Events –
in order with detail

The rocket had two distinct sections: the lunar module, named *Eagle* by the crew, which was to separate from the main craft and take Armstrong and Aldrin to the moon's surface; and *Columbia*, the command module, which was piloted by Collins.

At 9.32 am, the rocket was launched into the sky. By 9.35 am, it had disappeared from view.

Four days later, Armstrong and Aldrin crawled into *Eagle* through a tunnel in the rocket. *Eagle* separated from *Columbia* and travelled towards the moon's surface while *Columbia* orbited the moon until it was time to re-engage with *Eagle*. Twelve minutes away from landing, panic struck. Lights flashing on the cockpit console indicated the computer was overloaded. Armstrong and Aldrin waited nervously for instructions from Mission Control in Houston, Texas. **Minutes later**, the order came through to keep going.

As they came closer to the surface, the astronauts **saw** that the Sea of Tranquillity, where they were due to land, was a mass of rocks and boulders. Armstrong had to find a clear spot or he would risk breaking one of the craft's landing legs. With only 20 seconds of fuel left, he landed the craft safely. All over the world, people **heard** Armstrong's words:

'Houston, Tranquillity Base here. The *Eagle* has landed!'

Armstrong and Aldrin, dressed in their moon suits, were eager to perform one of the most significant events in world history. With a television camera attached to his equipment, the whole world witnessed Neil Armstrong step backwards from *Eagle* and take the first step on the moon. As he did so, he uttered his most famous quote:

'That's one small step for man ... one giant leap for mankind'.

As Aldrin followed, he declared in awe:

'Beautiful! Beautiful! **Magnificent desolation**!'

Following tradition, Armstrong and Aldrin planted their national flag to indicate that the United States of America was the first nation to land on the moon. They also left a plaque which read:

We came in peace for all mankind.

For two hours, the astronauts took photographs, collected samples and set up experiments. It was then time to be picked up by Collins in *Columbia*. Once back on board, *Eagle* was **discarded** and *Columbia* headed for home.

On 24 July, after eight days in space, the craft re-entered Earth's atmosphere and splashed down in the Pacific Ocean. Mission accomplished; the space race to the moon was over.

Conclusion –
indicating value of event

In the years since space exploration began, there have been great successes and disastrous failures in the quest for greater knowledge and understanding of our planet's solar system. But for as long as resources will allow, exploration beyond our planet is set to continue.

Right-side margin notes:
- appropriate paragraphing
- vocabulary to suggest passing of time; e.g. **Four days later, Minutes later**
- verbs in the past tense; **saw, heard**
- varied and interesting vocabulary; e.g. **Magnificent desolation, discarded**

Teacher information

- Discuss what a recount is, explaining that it can be presented in many different forms.
- Read and discuss the recount on page 23 with the pupils.
- Discuss the different sections of the framework and ensure pupils understand how the text fits into each.
- Emphasise the language features listed to the right of the text above.
- Work through the analysis on page 24 with the pupils.
- Plan a similar recount, writing ideas for each section of the framework and discuss and model how the plan is transformed into a coherent piece of text.
- Pupils use page 25 to plan and then write a recount about a major event in history of technology; e.g. first flight of the supersonic aircraft, *Concorde*, in 1969; the discovery of King Tutankhamun's tomb in 1923 by Lord Carnarvon.
- Pupils choose an event relevant to a topic currently being studied. (Context)

- Categorise work into subject areas—e.g. technology, science, history, sport—and present in a class book divided into these areas. This could be used as an information resource for other classes. (Publishing/Purpose/Audience)
- Display work under the headings of the different areas with accompanying illustrations and photographs. (Display)

Answers

Page 24

1. Teacher check
2. When? – Wednesday 16 July 1969
   Where? – NASA launch pad, Kennedy Space Centre, Florida
   Who? – Neil Armstrong, Edwin Aldrin, Michael Collins
   Why? – launch of *Apollo 11* in space race between USA and USSR
3. Teacher check
4. Teacher check

SPACE RACE

On Wednesday 16 July 1969, the space rocket, *Apollo 11* stood on the NASA launch pad at the Kennedy Space Centre in Florida. It was hoped that its success would crown the USA as leaders in the space race, ahead of the USSR. Seven months earlier, Neil Armstrong, Edwin Buzz Aldrin and Michael Collins had been named as the astronauts to man the craft on its historic voyage.

The rocket had two distinct sections: the lunar module, named *Eagle* by the crew, which was to separate from the main craft and take Armstrong and Aldrin to the moon's surface; and *Columbia*, the command module, which was piloted by Collins.

At 9.32 am, the rocket was launched into the sky. By 9.35 am, it had disappeared from view.

Four days later, Armstrong and Aldrin crawled into *Eagle* through a tunnel in the rocket. *Eagle* separated from *Columbia* and travelled towards the moon's surface while *Columbia* orbited the moon until it was time to re-engage with *Eagle*. Twelve minutes away from landing, panic struck. Lights flashing on the cockpit console indicated the computer was overloaded. Armstrong and Aldrin waited nervously for instructions from Mission Control in Houston, Texas. Minutes later, the order came through to keep going.

As they came closer to the surface, the astronauts saw that the Sea of Tranquillity, where they were due to land, was a mass of rocks and boulders. Armstrong had to find a clear spot or he would risk breaking one of the craft's landing legs. With only 20 seconds of fuel left, he landed the craft safely. All over the world, people heard Armstrong's words:

'Houston, Tranquillity Base here. The *Eagle* has landed!'

Armstrong and Aldrin, dressed in their moon suits, were eager to perform one of the most significant events in world history. With a television camera attached to his equipment, the whole world witnessed Neil Armstrong step backwards from *Eagle* and take the first step on the moon. As he did so, he uttered his most famous quote:

'That's one small step for man ... one giant leap for mankind'.

As Aldrin followed, he declared in awe:

'Beautiful! Beautiful! Magnificent desolation!'

Following tradition, Armstrong and Aldrin planted their national flag to indicate that the United States of America was the first nation to land on the moon. They also left a plaque which read:

We came in peace for all mankind.

For two hours, the astronauts took photographs, collected samples and set up experiments. It was then time to be picked up by Collins in *Columbia*. Once back on board, *Eagle* was discarded and *Columbia* headed for home.

On 24 July, after eight days in space, the craft re-entered Earth's atmosphere and splashed down in the Pacific Ocean. Mission accomplished; the space race to the moon was over.

In the years since space exploration began, there have been great successes and disastrous failures in the quest for greater knowledge and understanding of our planet's solar system. But for as long as resources will allow, exploration beyond our planet is set to continue.

Use the recount on page 23 to complete the page.

1. Title

(a) Do you think the title reflects the content of the text? **yes** ☐ **no** ☐

(b) Suggest an alternative title.

2. Orientation

What information does the orientation provide?

3. Events

In your own words, rewrite the events as they occurred for Armstrong and Aldrin, while they were in *Eagle,* before the landing or while they were on the moon.

4. Conclusion

Using the past tense, describe how each man might have felt about his role in the success of the mission.

Neil Armstrong	**Buzz Aldrin**	**Michael Collins**

1. Plan a recount of a major event in history.

Title

Orientation

Events

Conclusion

2. Write your recount.

3. Edit your work.

Structural and language features are shown on the left and right of the text below.

Title	**Roast pumpkin and bacon salad**
Goal – the purpose of the procedure	Follow this recipe to create a delicious summer salad!
Materials – the materials required to complete the procedure	Ingredients: • 1 kg pumpkin (butternut is best) • 6 slices bacon • 200 g baby spinach leaves • 1/2 cup parmesan cheese • 200 g snow peas • 1/3 cup pine nuts • 4 garlic cloves • 1 tablespoon olive oil • salt and pepper Dressing: • 2 tablespoons olive oil • 2 tablespoons red wine vinegar • 2 teaspoons Dijon mustard • **1 teaspoon sugar** • 2 teaspoons fresh thyme	Utensils: • baking dish • frying pan • sharp knife • absorbent paper • screw-top jar • large bowl • tongs • measuring cups • measuring spoons • cheese shaver • salad servers
Method – clear steps in a logical order	Method: 1. Pre-heat oven to 190 °C. 2. Peel pumpkin carefully. Chop into 3-centimetre cubes. 3. Place pumpkin in baking dish. **Drizzle** with olive oil. **Sprinkle** salt and pepper to taste. 4. **Peel garlic cloves**. Add to baking dish. 5. Bake pumpkin in oven for 35 minutes. Use tongs to turn occasionally. Remove when tender and brown. 6. **Remove rind from bacon**. 7. Cook bacon in greased pan until brown and crisp. Remove from pan and drain on absorbent paper. Crumble into bite-size pieces. 8. Wash snow peas and baby spinach leaves under cold water. **Drain** well. 9. Toast pine nuts in greased pan until light brown in colour. Drain on absorbent paper. 10. Shave parmesan cheese (if not pre-shaved). 11. **Measure** olive oil, red wine vinegar, Dijon mustard, sugar and thyme and place in screw-top jar. **Shake** dressing well. 12. Toss warm pumpkin with bacon gently in large bowl. Add baby spinach, snow peas, cheese and nuts. Toss with salad servers until combined. 13. Drizzle dressing over salad.	
Test – an evaluation	Test your salad by tasting it!

• clear concise information— unnecessary words omitted; e.g. **1 teaspoon sugar**, **Peel garlic cloves**

• subject-specific vocabulary; e.g. **Drizzle**, **Sprinkle**

• the present tense is used; e.g. **Remove rind from bacon**, **Drain**

• command verbs used in instructions; e.g. **Measure**, **Shake**

Teacher information

• Collect a variety of recipe books. Distribute to students in small groups and give them the task of defining the structure of a recipe. Groups report back to the class.

• Students read the text on page 27. The text could be enlarged using the accompanying CD on an interactive whiteboard. Discuss each section of the procedure.

• Focus on the language of the text. Note that unnecessary words (such as 'the') are omitted. The steps are written simply and concisely, and they are easy to follow.

• The first word of each step in the method is a directing verb. These types of verbs are called command verbs (imperatives). Ask students for more examples of command verbs found in the text.

• Discuss which tense is being used in the procedure and ask for students to give examples of this. (Present tense)

• Work through the analysis on page 28 with the class.

• Before students attempt to plan and write their procedure, model this process to the class. Write a plan for a procedure to make a familiar recipe, such as spaghetti bolognaise. Emphasise that the first word of the method will often be a command verb such as 'Chop', 'Slice', 'Sprinkle' etc.

• Demonstrate to the class how to use the plan on page 29 to write the procedure.

• Once the students' recipes have been planned and written, they should be proofread and edited. Students publish their

recipes using a word processor. Collate the recipes to make a class recipe book. (Publish/Purpose/Audience)

• Choose a recipe to follow and make during a cooking lesson. (Purpose/Context)

• Use a digital camera to take photographs of each step of the new recipe being made. Enlarge the procedure for the recipe to A3 and attach the photographs to each step. Discuss sequencing with the class. (Display/Publish/Context)

Answers

Page 28

1. Teacher check

2. To make a roast pumpkin and bacon salad for summer.

3. (a) red—salt and pepper, 4 garlic cloves, 200 g snow peas, 1/3 cup pine nuts; blue—1 teaspoon sugar, 2 teaspoons fresh thyme; green—screw-top jar, large bowl

   (b) Answers will vary

   (c) The ingredients are listed before the method so that they can be collected prior to starting the procedure.

4. (a) command

   (b) Teacher check

   (c) Teacher check

5. The recipe is a success if it tastes good.

Roast pumpkin and bacon salad

Follow this recipe to create a delicious summer salad!

Ingredients:

Salad:

- 1 kg pumpkin (butternut is best)
- 6 slices bacon
- 200 g baby spinach leaves
- $\frac{1}{2}$ cup parmesan cheese
- 200 g snow peas
- $\frac{1}{3}$ cup pine nuts
- 4 garlic cloves
- 1 tablespoon olive oil
- salt and pepper

Dressing:

- 2 tablespoons olive oil
- 2 tablespoons red wine vinegar
- 2 teaspoons Dijon mustard
- 1 teaspoon sugar
- 2 teaspoons fresh thyme

Utensils:

baking dish

frying pan

sharp knife

absorbent paper

screw-top jar

large bowl

tongs

measuring cups

measuring spoons

cheese shaver

salad servers

Method:

1. Pre-heat oven to 190 °C.
2. Peel pumpkin carefully. Chop into 3-centimetre cubes.
3. Place pumpkin in baking dish. Drizzle with olive oil. Sprinkle salt and pepper to taste.
4. Peel garlic cloves. Add to baking dish.
5. Bake pumpkin in oven for 35 minutes. Use tongs to turn occasionally. Remove when tender and brown.
6. Remove rind from bacon.
7. Cook bacon in greased pan until brown and crisp. Remove from pan and drain on absorbent paper. Crumble into bite-size pieces.
8. Wash snow peas and baby spinach leaves under cold water. Drain well.
9. Toast pine nuts in greased pan until light brown in colour. Drain on absorbent paper.
10. Shave parmesan cheese (if not pre-shaved).
11. Measure olive oil, red wine vinegar, Dijon mustard, sugar and thyme and place in screw-top jar. Shake dressing well.
12. Toss warm pumpkin with bacon gently in large bowl. Add baby spinach, snow peas, cheese and nuts. Toss with salad servers until combined.
13. Drizzle dressing over salad.

Test your salad by tasting it!

Use the procedure on page 27 to complete the page.

1. Title

Why should the title clearly state what a procedure is about?

2. Goal

What is the goal of this procedure?

3. Ingredients

(a) Colour the main salad ingredients red, dressing ingredients blue and utensils green.

screw-top jar	1 teaspoon sugar
salt and pepper	4 garlic cloves
2 teaspoons fresh thyme	large bowl
200 g snow peas	$\frac{1}{3}$ cup pine nuts

(b) Complete the sentence.

The ingredients for the dressing are listed separately to the main salad ingredients so ...

_____

_____

_____

(c) Why are the ingredients and utensils listed before the method?

_____

_____

_____

4. Method

(a) The first word in each step of the method is a directing verb called a _____ verb.

(b) Find at least six examples of command verbs in the text that are not the first word of each step. Write them in the box.

Procedures are written using clear, concise information. Unnecessary words are not included.

(c) Find two sentences in the method that are good examples of this. Copy them below.

• _____

_____

_____

• _____

_____

_____

5. Test

How will you know if the recipe is a success?

_____

1. Plan a procedure for a recipe you are familiar with or for a different type of salad.

Title

Goal

Ingredients

Utensils

Method

Concisely written, numbered steps in correct order.

Test

How will you test if the recipe is successful?

2. Write your procedure.

3. Edit your work.

Procedures

TEACHERS NOTES

Structural and language features are shown on the left and right of the text below.

Title		
	Recycling paper	
Goal – the purpose of the procedure	Follow the instructions to produce writing paper from newspaper.	• subject-specific vocabulary; e.g. **bleach**, **funnel**
Materials – the materials required to complete the procedure	Materials: • water • soft drink bottle with lid • rubber band • metal spoon • 100 mL **bleach** • **funnel** • wooden board • large jar • 2 dishcloths (to act as sieve) • newspaper • dishwashing detergent • measuring jug • rolling pin • tea towel	• clear concise information—unnecessary words omitted; **Wash hands thoroughly**, **Leave overnight**
Method – clear steps in a logical order	Method: 1. Rip newspaper page in half and tear into small pieces. 2. Wash and dry drink bottle. Poke newspaper into bottle. 3. Use jug to measure 100 mL of bleach carefully. 4. Insert funnel in bottle and add bleach slowly. Warning: Do not smell bleach. Wear gloves to clean spills. **Wash hands thoroughly**. 5. Secure lid and shake bottle for four minutes. **Leave overnight**. 6. Fill bottle with water. Secure lid and shake for four minutes. 7. Wash and dry jar. Place dishcloths over jar and secure with rubber band. 8. Pour mixture from bottle onto cloth. 9. Use back of spoon to carefully press mixture into cloth. Liquid separates from mixture and enters jar. Solid (pulp) remains on cloth. 10. **Scrape** pulp into bottle. **Fill** with water and add five drops of dishwashing detergent. **Attach** lid and shake gently. 11. Pour mixture through cloth and press with spoon. 12. Repeat steps 10 and 11 until pulp is clean. 13. Scrape pulp from cloth. Standing above sink, use hands to squeeze all water from pulp. 14. **Press** pulp onto board and flatten with hand. Roll flat with rolling pin. 15. **Shape** pulp into rectangle shape and allow to dry.	• command verbs used in instructions; e.g. **Scrape**, **Fill**, **Attach** • the present tense is used; e.g. **Press**, **Shape**
Test – an evaluation	Results: Paper is ready when completely dry. Paper is now white and can be used as writing paper. Give paper a quality rating. Five stars—exceptional quality, one star—poor quality.	

Teacher information

- Ask the class to think about science experiments they have conducted. What are the main components of a science experiment procedure? Discuss.
- Students read the text on page 31.
- Focus on the language of the text. Note that unnecessary words (such as 'the') are omitted. The steps are written simply and clearly and are easy to follow.
- The first word of each step in the method is a directing verb. These types of verbs are called command verbs (imperatives). Ask students for more examples of command verbs found in the text.
- Discuss which tense is being used in the procedure and ask for students to give examples of this. (Present tense)
- Work through the analysis on page 32 with the class.
- Before students attempt to plan and write their procedure, model this process to the class. Write a plan for a simple science procedure such as showing that liquids evaporate when heated (by the sun). Model using the plan to write the procedure. Demonstrate how to omit unnecessary words from sentences so the language used is concise.
- Students plan their science procedures using the plan on page 33.
- Once the students 'separating substances' science procedures are written, they should be proofread and edited. Students publish their procedures using a word processor and display them. Each procedure should include a scientific diagram with the materials labelled. (Publish/Display)

- Choose a student's science procedure for the whole class to follow. Use a digital camera to photograph the students conducting the experiment. Display the photographs with an enlarged copy of the procedure. (Purpose/Display)
- Hold small-group discussions about the strengths and weaknesses of the procedure. Ask for positive criticisms for the author on how to improve the procedure. (Purpose/Audience)
- 'Recycling' and 'separating substances' are investigations that can be conducted as part of discovering the properties of natural and processed materials in science. Recycling is also an important concept taught when studying the environment. (Context/Purpose)

Answers

Page 32
1. (a)–(b) Answers will vary
2. (a) produce writing paper from newspaper.
   (b) goal
3. (a) yes
   (b) If a material is left off the list, the procedure cannot be followed correctly.
   (c) Teacher check
   (d) Answers will vary
   (e)–(f) Teacher check
4. Paper will be completely dry, clean and white so it can be used as writing paper.

Recycling paper

Follow the instructions to produce writing paper from newspaper.

Materials:

- water
- soft drink bottle with lid
- metal spoon
- funnel
- wooden board

- large jar
- 2 dishcloths (to act as sieve)
- dishwashing detergent
- rolling pin
- tea towel

- rubber band
- newspaper
- measuring jug
- 100 mL bleach

Method:

1. Rip newspaper page in half and tear into small pieces.
2. Wash and dry drink bottle. Poke newspaper into bottle.
3. Use jug to measure 100 mL of bleach carefully.
4. Insert funnel in bottle and add bleach slowly.

   Warning: Do not smell bleach. Wear gloves to clean spills. Wash hands thoroughly.
5. Secure lid and shake bottle for four minutes. Leave overnight.
6. Fill bottle with water. Secure lid and shake for four minutes.
7. Wash and dry jar. Place dishcloths over jar and secure with rubber band.

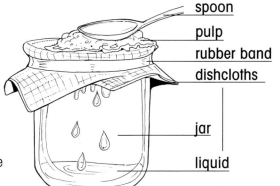

spoon
pulp
rubber band
dishcloths

jar

liquid

8. Pour mixture from bottle onto cloth.
9. Use back of spoon to carefully press mixture into cloth. Liquid separates from mixture and enters jar. Solid (pulp) remains on cloth.
10. Scrape pulp into bottle. Fill with water and add five drops of dishwashing detergent. Attach lid and shake gently.
11. Pour mixture through cloth and press with spoon.
12. Repeat steps 10 and 11 until pulp is clean.
13. Scrape pulp from cloth. Standing above sink, use hands to squeeze all water from pulp.
14. Press pulp onto board and flatten with hand. Roll flat with rolling pin.
15. Shape pulp into rectangle shape and allow to dry.

Results:

Paper is ready when completely dry. Paper is now white and can be used as writing paper. Give paper a quality rating. Five stars—exceptional quality, one star—poor quality.

Use the procedure on page 31 to complete the page.

1. Title

(a) Is the title of the procedure appropriate? **yes** ☐ **no** ☐

(b) Write an alternative title that would suit this procedure.

2. Goal

(a) The aim of the procedure is to

_____

_____

(b) The aim is the objective of the procedure.

Another name for an aim is a g_____

3. Ingredients

(a) The materials are set out as lists using bullet points. **yes** ☐ **no** ☐

(b) What would happen if one of the materials was left off the list?

_____

_____

(c) Illustrate three of the main steps of the method in the boxes below. Write the number of the step in the smaller box. Label the materials in each diagram.

(d) Do you think diagrams demonstrating some of the steps of the procedure would be useful? **yes** ☐ **no** ☐

Explain. _____

_____

(e) Procedures are written using the present tense. Copy two sentences that show this.

- _____

- _____

(f) Choose one sentence and rewrite it using the past tense.

4. Test

How will you know your paper has been recycled successfully?

_____

1. Plan a science procedure to investigate how mixtures of solids and liquids can be separated.

Title

Aim

Materials

Method

Concisely written, numbered steps in order.

Results

How should the results be recorded?

2. Write your procedure.   **3.** Edit your work.

Structural and language features are shown on the left and right of the text below.

Title		Diamond kite	

Goal – the purpose of the procedure	Construct a kite that flies.

Materials – the materials required to complete the procedure	What you need: • large ball of thick string (such as butcher cord) • tape • craft glue • strong paper—102 cm square • 2 strong bamboo sticks or wooden dowelling—90 cm and 102 cm • small handsaw • paint or felt-tip pens • ribbons of different colours cut to same length • scissors

Method – clear steps in a logical order	What to do: 1. Place shorter stick horizontally across longer stick at right angles to make cross shape. Ensure longer stick is in centre of shorter stick. 2. **Add glue to join area**. Cut 20 cm string. Tie join area, winding string around join a number of times. Trim ends. 3. Saw grooves across ends of both sticks (four grooves in total). Groove must be deep enough to hold string in place. 4. **Measure** string to reach around kite frame with some spare. **Cut** string. 5. Place kite frame flat with string around it. Start at top of frame and make loop from string near top groove. **Attach by wrapping** string around stick. 6. Stretch string to left of frame and guide into groove. 7. Stretch string to bottom of frame and make loop. Attach by wrapping string around stick. 8. **Stretch string** to right of frame and guide into groove. 9. Wrap end of string around top of stick and tape down. Cut off unnecessary string. Note: String must be taut but not bending kite frame. 10. Place kite frame face down on paper and cut around it, leaving 3-cm margin. Fold edges over frame and tape securely. 11. Cut new piece of string 122 cm long. Tie ends to top and bottom loop (see diagram). 12. Create loop in string above intersection of kite frame. This string is called the '**bridle**'. It helps control kite. 13. Attach free end of remaining ball of string to bridle through loop created above intersection of kite frame. This string is the '**flying line**' to fly kite. 14. Cut new length of string to create tail. Tie colourful ribbons at 10-cm intervals along tail. Tie top of tail to loop at bottom of kite frame. 15. Decorate kite using paints or felt-tip pens.

Test – an evaluation	Test kite by taking it outside on light to moderately windy day. Find open area away from power lines and trees. Hold kite in both hands. Toss lightly into wind or let out small length of string and run with kite behind you. If kite is 'unstable' increase tail. If it 'sinks', decrease tail.

Right margin notes:
• clear concise information— unnecessary words omitted; **Add glue to join area**

• the present tense is used; e.g. **Attach by wrapping**, **Stretch string**

• command verbs used in instructions; e.g. **Measure**, **Cut**

• subject-specific vocabulary; e.g. **bridle**, **flying line**

Teacher information

• Ask students to think of objects they have made by following instructions such as models, construction toys, craft items etc. What is usually included in the instructions? Discuss.

• Read the text on page 35 with the class. The text could be enlarged using the accompanying CD on an interactive whiteboard. Discuss each section of the procedure. Ask students if they have made kites previously. Did they follow similar instructions?

• Focus on the language of the text. Note that unnecessary words (such as 'the') are omitted. The steps are written simply and clearly and are easy to follow.

• The first word of each step in the method is a directing verb. These types of verbs are called command verbs (imperatives). Ask students for more examples of command verbs found in the text.

• Work through the analysis on page 36 with the class.

• Before students attempt to plan and write their procedure, model this process to the class. Write a plan for a procedure to make a simple craft item such as a spinner (colourful circular card with a toothpick pushed through centre) or a finger puppet.

• Show the class how to use the plan to write the procedure. Demonstrate omitting unnecessary words from the text so that the language used is concise.

• Students use the plan on page 37 to plan their procedure. Once written, they are proofread and edited. Students publish their procedures using a word processor. Collate the procedures to make a class craft book. (Publish/Purpose/Audience)

• Choose a procedure to follow and make with the class. Use a digital camera to photograph the students making the craft items and display. (Purpose/Display)

• Organise for students to give their procedures to students in younger classes, who must follow them precisely. Did the finished products look as the writers intended? Why/Why not? Analyse procedures to find where instructions were not clear. (Purpose)

Answers

Page 36
1. (a) Diamond kite   (b) Answers will vary
2. Yes
3. (a) Yes
   (b) The materials are listed before the method so that they can be collected prior to starting the procedure.
4. (a) The steps are numbered to show that they must be followed in order.
   (b) The order of the steps is important as each must be completed before the next is started.
   (c) Tie ends to top and bottom loops (see diagram).
   (d) Answers will vary
   (e) Answers will vary. Possible answer: More diagrams included.
5. (a) During light to moderate winds in an open area.
   (b) Kite will fly.

Diamond Kite

Construct a kite that flies.

What you need:

- large ball of thick string (such as butcher cord)
- tape
- craft glue
- strong paper—102 cm square
- 2 strong bamboo sticks or wooden dowelling—90 cm and 102 cm
- small handsaw
- paint or felt-tip pens
- ribbons of different colours cut to same length
- scissors

Diagram showing back of diamond kite

string sits in groove on end of stick

groove
loop in string
bridle
102 cm stick
join
groove
loop in bridle
90 cm stick
flying line
tape
3 cm fold over string
ribbon
groove
loop in string

What to do:

1. Place shorter stick horizontally across longer stick at right angles to make cross shape. Ensure longer stick is in centre of shorter stick.

2. Add glue to join area. Cut 20 cm string. Tie join area, winding string around join a number of times. Trim ends.

3. Saw grooves across ends of both sticks (four grooves in total). Groove must be deep enough to hold string in place.

4. Measure string to reach around kite frame with some spare. Cut string.

5. Place kite frame flat with string around it. Start at top of frame and make loop from string near top groove. Attach by wrapping string around stick.

6. Stretch string to left of frame and guide into groove.

7. Stretch string to bottom of frame and make loop. Attach by wrapping string around stick.

8. Stretch string to right of frame and guide into groove.

9. Wrap end of string around top of stick and tape down. Cut off unnecessary string. Note: String must be taut but not bending kite frame.

10. Place kite frame face down on paper and cut around it, leaving 3-cm margin. Fold edges over frame and tape securely.

11. Cut new piece of string 122 cm long. Tie ends to top and bottom loop (see diagram).

12. Create loop in string above intersection of kite frame. This string is called the 'bridle'. It helps control kite.

13. Attach free end of remaining ball of string to bridle through loop created above intersection of kite frame. This string is the 'flying line' to fly kite.

14. Cut new length of string to create tail. Tie colourful ribbons at 10-cm intervals along tail. Tie top of tail to loop at bottom of kite frame.

15. Decorate kite using paints or felt-tip pens.

Test kite by taking it outside on light to moderately windy day. Find open area away from power lines and trees. Hold kite in both hands. Toss lightly into wind or let out small length of string and run with kite behind you. If kite is 'unstable' increase tail. If it 'sinks', decrease tail.

Use the procedure on page 35 to complete the page.

1. Title

(a) The title of the procedure is

(b) Write another suitable title.

2. Goal

The goal states the purpose of the procedure. **yes** ☐ **no** ☐

3. What you need

(a) The materials are set out as a list using bullet points. **yes** ☐ **no** ☐

(b) Why are the materials listed before the method? _____

_____

_____

4. What to do

(a) Why are the steps in the method numbered?

(b) Explain why the order of the steps is important.

(c) Procedures are written clearly so they can be easily followed. Unnecessary words are not included. Rewrite this sentence removing all unnecessary words.

Tie one end of the string to the loop at the top of the kite frame and the other end of the string to the loop at the bottom of the kite frame (see the diagram for more instruction).

(d) Colour how easily you could follow this procedure to construct a diamond kite.

impossible!   **only with help**   **muddled through**   **quite easily**   **piece of cake!**

(e) Offer the writer of the procedure some suggestions to make the instructions easier to follow.

_____

_____

5. Test

(a) When and where should the diamond kite be tested?

(b) How will you know if the procedure has been followed correctly?

1. Plan a procedure to construct a simple craft item you are familiar with, such as a mask.

Title

Goal

What you need

What to do (Method)

Concisely written, numbered steps in order.

Test

How will you know if the procedure is a success?

2. Write your procedure.   **3.** Edit your work.

Structural and language features are shown on the left and right of the text below.

	Aquatic biomes	
Title – states what is being reported		• written in timeless present tense; **are adapted, covers**
Classification – a general statement about the subject of the report	A biome is a large area of distinctive plant and animal groups that are **adapted** to that physical environment. There are two main types of biomes—aquatic (water) and terrestrial (land). Most of the Earth is made up of aquatic biomes as water **covers** nearly 75 per cent of its surface.	
Description – provides accurate description and facts	Aquatic biomes can be divided into two categories—freshwater and marine. Freshwater biomes usually have a salt concentration of less than one per cent, while marine biomes have a salt concentration that averages three per cent. **Freshwater biomes** include ponds, lakes, rivers, streams and wetlands. Marine biomes include oceans, coral reefs and **estuaries**.	• technical vocabulary and subject-specific terms are used; e.g. **Freshwater biomes, estuaries**
	Ponds and lakes have two distinct zones that are home to different plants and animals. The warm, shallow zone is home to life such as reeds, water lilies, snails, insects, birds, carp, crustaceans and amphibians. In the deeper, darker, colder zone, crustaceans and fish can be found feeding on dead plankton.	
	Rivers and streams have water that is constantly flowing and is much colder than water in ponds and lakes. Freshwater fish such as salmon, trout and catfish can be found, along with floating weed, algae, fungi and mosses.	• uses factual language rather than imaginative; e.g. **vary in temperature, is highly pressurised**
	Wetlands include marshes, swamps and bogs and usually support the largest variety of freshwater plant and animal species. Their still waters and humid environment are home to lilies; some trees; birds such as ducks, pelicans and herons; snakes and other reptiles; mammals and insects.	
	Oceans are the largest and most diverse of all the aquatic biomes. They have different zones that **vary in temperature** according to the amount of sunlight they receive. The warmer, tidal zone near the shore contains plants and animals that must cope with the rising and falling tides. The open ocean is host to many fish, crustaceans, sea turtles, marine mammals, seaweed and plankton. Very little plant life is found in the cold, dark, deep ocean, but sponges, starfish, anemones and squid dwell there. The extremely cold, deep and pitch black abyssal zone **is highly pressurised** and some unusual varieties of fish, eels and squid can be found there.	• written in the third person; e.g. **Coral reefs, They**
	Coral reefs are found in warm, shallow waters, usually near land. **They** are formed by tiny animals called 'polyps' that live in colonies. When the coral polyps die, they leave a hard, limestone skeleton that builds up over time to form a coral reef. A wide variety of animals and plants are found here including sponges, sea urchins, plankton, starfish, reef fish, sharks, octopus, sea turtles and molluscs.	
	Estuaries occur where a river or stream merges with the ocean, creating a mixture of fresh and salt water. Many fish lay their eggs in this still, murky water. Waterfowl such as heron, geese and ducks can be found, as well as mangroves, reeds, algae, oysters, crabs and insects.	• information is organised into paragraphs
Conclusion – a final comment about the subject of the report. (It may include a personal comment by the writer.)	Aquatic biomes have been the subject of interest and extensive research for many years. The rich diversity of environments and plant and animal life should continue to capture the imagination and interest of all of us, well into the future.	

Teacher information

- Read through the information report with the pupils and discuss the features of a report.
- Work through the analysis on page 40 with the class.

  Explain that: 'I', 'we', 'my' and 'our' are examples of the **first person**

  'you' and 'your' are examples of the **second person**

  'he', 'she', 'it' and 'they' are examples of the **third person**

  For example: I/We visit my/our grandparents every week. (first person)

  You visit your grandparents every week. (second person)

  Adam/He visits his grandparents every week. /They visit their grandparents every week. (third person)

- Before pupils attempt to plan and write their own information report on page 41, model this process with the whole class, using an animal or plant as a subject. Pupils will need to have gathered sufficient information about the aquatic or terrestrial biome of their choice prior to planning their report.
- Pupils' reports could be read out orally by them in small groups or to the whole class and discussed. (Purpose/Audience)
- Published reports, accompanied with appropriate illustrations or photographs, could be displayed for other

pupils to read and compare, especially those who chose the same biome. (Publishing/Display/Purpose)
- The activity could be done in conjunction with the science curriculum. (Context/Purpose)

Answers

Page 40

1. Teacher check
2. They are more common because water covers nearly 75 per cent of the Earth's surface.
3. (a) freshwater – ponds, lakes, streams, rivers or wetlands

   marine – oceans, coral reefs and estuaries

   (b) Answers will vary but should include words such as coral reef, polyps, colonies, limestone skeleton, starfish etc.

   (c) The answer should indicate that it is describing the zones in the ocean and the plant and animal life found in each.

   (d) have, is flowing, is

   (e) **Wetlands** include marshes, swamps and bogs and **their** still waters and humid environment are home to a large variety of plant and animal species.
4. Because the rich diversity of environments and plant and animal life should continue to capture the imagination and interest of people.

Aquatic biomes

A biome is a large area of distinctive plant and animal groups that are adapted to that physical environment. There are two main types of biomes—aquatic (water) and terrestrial (land). Most of the Earth is made up of aquatic biomes as water covers nearly 75 per cent of its surface.

Aquatic biomes can be divided into two categories—freshwater and marine. Freshwater biomes usually have a salt concentration of less than one per cent, while marine biomes have a salt concentration that averages three per cent. Freshwater biomes include ponds, lakes, rivers, streams and wetlands. Marine biomes include oceans, coral reefs and estuaries.

Ponds and lakes have two distinct zones that are home to different plants and animals. The warm, shallow zone is home to life such as reeds, water lilies, snails, insects, birds, carp, crustaceans and amphibians. In the deeper, darker, colder zone, crustaceans and fish can be found feeding on dead plankton.

Rivers and streams have water that is constantly flowing and is much colder than water in ponds and lakes. Freshwater fish such as salmon, trout and catfish can be found, along with floating weed, algae, fungi and mosses.

Wetlands include marshes, swamps and bogs and usually support the largest variety of freshwater plant and animal species. Their still waters and humid environment are home to lilies; some trees; birds such as ducks, pelicans and herons; snakes and other reptiles; mammals and insects.

Oceans are the largest and most diverse of all the aquatic biomes. They have different zones that vary in temperature according to the amount of sunlight they receive. The warmer, tidal zone near the shore contains plants and animals that must cope with the rising and falling tides. The open ocean is host to many fish, crustaceans, sea turtles, marine mammals, seaweed and plankton. Very little plant life is found in the cold, dark, deep ocean, but sponges, starfish, anemones and squid dwell there. The extremely cold, deep and pitch black abyssal zone is highly pressurised and some unusual varieties of fish, eels and squid can be found there.

Coral reefs are found in warm, shallow waters, usually near land. They are formed by tiny animals called 'polyps' that live in colonies. When the coral polyps die, they leave a hard, limestone skeleton that builds up over time to form a coral reef. A wide variety of animals and plants are found here including sponges, sea urchins, plankton, starfish, reef fish, sharks, octopus, sea turtles and molluscs.

Estuaries occur where a river or stream merges with the ocean, creating a mixture of fresh and salt water. Many fish lay their eggs in this still, murky water. Waterfowl such as heron, geese and ducks can be found, as well as mangroves, reeds, algae, oysters, crabs and insects.

Aquatic biomes have been the subject of interest and extensive research for many years. The rich diversity of environments and plant and animal life should continue to capture the imagination and interest of all of us, well into the future.

Use the report on page 39 to complete the page.

1. Title

(a) Why does a report need a title?

_____

_____

_____

(b) What features should it have?

2. Classification

Why are aquatic biomes more common than terrestrial biomes?

3. Description

(a) List three examples of each biome.

freshwater

marine

(b) List four examples of subject-specific language in paragraph 6 of the description section.

_____   _____

_____   _____

(c) What is the main idea of paragraph 5 in the description section?

_____

_____

_____

(d) Highlight the present tense verbs in this sentence.

Rivers and streams have water that is constantly flowing and is much colder than water in ponds and lakes.

(e) This sentence about **wetlands** has been written in the first person. Change it so it is written in the third person.

We include marshes, swamps and bogs and our still waters and humid environment are home to a large variety of plant and animal species.

_____

_____

4. Conclusion

Why does the writer think people will continue to study aquatic biomes?

_____

_____

1. Plan an information report about a specific aquatic or terrestrial biome. Remember to write in the present tense, include accurate facts and use vocabulary specific to your subject.

Title

Classification

A general statement about the subject.

Description

Divide the description into sections.

Conclusion

It may contain a personal opinion.

2. Write your report.

3. Edit your work.

Structural and language features are shown on the left and right of the text below.

Title – states what is being reported	**Ancient Egypt**

• uses factual language rather than imaginative; e.g. **Located in north-east Africa, water for irrigation**

Classification – a general statement about the subject of the report	Ancient Egypt was the site of one of the world's first civilisations, arising about 5000 years ago. It was also one of the longest surviving, lasting for more than 2000 years.

Description – provides accurate description and facts	**Located in north-east Africa**, Ancient Egypt stretched along a narrow strip of land through which the Nile River flowed. Each year the Nile overflowed, depositing rich, black soil along its banks. The Ancient Egyptians called this area 'Kemet' (the black land), and the desert around the valley 'Deshret' (the red land). Not only did the Nile River provide fertile soil for farming, it supplied **water for irrigation** and was Ancient Egypt's chief transportation route. The Greek historian, Herodotus, described Egypt as 'the gift of the Nile'.

Ancient Egypt was surrounded by natural boundaries that gave **it** protection from invading armies; impenetrable desert bordering the east, south and west and the Mediterranean Sea to the north. This isolation allowed Ancient Egypt to grow in its own way, without outside influences.

It is believed that between one to four million people lived in the valley at various times. The Ancient Egyptians had dark skin and hair and were of mixed descent, originating from north African and south-western Asian peoples. They spoke a language that was related to certain languages from these areas. It was written in **hieroglyphics**, a form of writing made up from more than 700 **picture symbols** of people, animals, plants or objects. It was written left to right, or right to left.

Ancient Egypt had three main classes of society. The upper class included the royal family, wealthy landowners or nobles, government officials, high-ranking priests and doctors. Merchants, craftworkers and manufacturers made up the middle class. The largest class was the lower class, of labourers.

Kings ruled Ancient Egypt. They **were succeeded** by the eldest son of their chief wife. But some chief wives only gave birth to daughters, so at least four of these claimed the right to the throne and became rulers. Some time in history the king became known as the 'pharaoh', an Egyptian word for 'great house'. The Ancient Egyptians believed the king had superhuman powers and made the Nile flood, the crops grow, protected his people and brought them good fortune.

The Ancient Egyptians **believed** that gods and goddesses influenced all aspects of nature and human activity. They also believed in the afterlife which was the reason great tombs and pyramids were built for kings and queens and smaller tombs for other Egyptians. The bodies of the dead were mummified to prevent them from decaying. They were placed in their tombs with items to use in the afterlife such as clothing, food, jewellery, furniture and mummified pets. |

• written in the third person; **Ancient Egypt, it**

• technical vocabulary and subject-specific terms are used; e.g. **hieroglyphics, picture symbols**

• this historical report is mainly written in the past tense; e.g. **were succeeded, believed**

Conclusion – a final comment about the subject of the report. (It may include a personal comment by the writer.)	The Ancient Egyptians are remembered for their important contributions to the development of civilisation in areas such as government, religion, farming methods and general lifestyle. The most obvious reminders of this civilisation are the pyramids—engineering and architectural marvels—still standing after 4500 years.

• information is organised into paragraphs

Teacher information

- Read through the historical report with the pupils and discuss the features of a report. Discuss how and why the past tense is needed in historical reports.
- Revise the third person (see page 38). Pupils complete the analysis on page 44.
- Before pupils attempt to plan and write their own historical report on page 45, model this process with the whole class, using another historical subject they are familiar with. Pupils will need to have gathered information about the civilisation of their choice prior to planning their report.
- Pupils' reports could be read out orally by them in small groups or to the whole class and discussed. (Purpose/Audience)
- Published reports, accompanied by appropriate illustrations, could be displayed for other pupils to read and compare, especially those who chose the same civilisation to report about. (Publishing/Display/Purpose)

Answers

Page 44
1. Teacher check
2. Teacher check
3. (a) (i)   the black land
      (ii) the red land
      (iii) a form of writing made up of picture symbols
      (iv) a king; from the ancient Egyptian word for 'great house'
      (v)   life after death
      (vi) specially treated to prevent decay
   (b) paragraph 3
   (c) Answers should indicate that it describes the main classes of society in Ancient Egypt.
   (d) is believed, originating
   (e) (i) first person
      (ii) **Ancient Egypt** was surrounded by natural boundaries that gave **it** protection from invading armies. This allowed **it** to grow in **its** own way, without outside influences.
4. Teacher check

Ancient Egypt

Ancient Egypt was the site of one of the world's first civilisations, arising about 5000 years ago. It was also one of the longest surviving, lasting for more than 2000 years.

Located in north-east Africa, Ancient Egypt stretched along a narrow strip of land through which the Nile River flowed. Each year the Nile overflowed, depositing rich, black soil along its banks. The Ancient Egyptians called this area 'Kemet' (the black land) and the desert around the valley 'Deshret' (the red land). Not only did the Nile River provide fertile soil for farming, it supplied water for irrigation and was Ancient Egypt's chief transportation route. The Greek historian, Herodotus, described Egypt as 'the gift of the Nile'.

Ancient Egypt was surrounded by natural boundaries that gave it protection from invading armies; impenetrable desert bordering the east, south and west and the Mediterranean Sea to the north. This isolation allowed Ancient Egypt to grow in its own way, without outside influences.

It is believed that between one to four million people lived in the valley at various times. The Ancient Egyptians had dark skin and hair and were of mixed descent, originating from north African and south-western Asian peoples. They spoke a language that was related to certain languages from these areas. It was written in hieroglyphics, a form of writing made up from more than 700 picture symbols of people, animals, plants or objects. It was written left to right, or right to left.

Ancient Egypt had three main classes of society. The upper class included the royal family, wealthy landowners or nobles, government officials, high-ranking priests and doctors. Merchants, craftworkers and manufacturers made up the middle class. The largest class was the lower class, of labourers.

Kings ruled Ancient Egypt. They were succeeded by the eldest son of their chief wife. But some chief wives only gave birth to daughters, so at least four of these claimed the right to the throne and became rulers. Some time in history the king became known as the 'pharaoh', an Egyptian word for 'great house'. The Ancient Egyptians believed the king had superhuman powers and made the Nile flood, the crops grow, protected his people and brought them good fortune.

The Ancient Egyptians believed that gods and goddesses influenced all aspects of nature and human activity. They also believed in the afterlife which was the reason great tombs and pyramids were built for kings and queens and smaller tombs for other Egyptians. The bodies of the dead were mummified to prevent them from decaying. They were placed in their tombs with items to use in the afterlife such as clothing, food, jewellery, furniture and mummified pets.

The Ancient Egyptians are remembered for their important contributions to the development of civilisation in areas such as government, religion, farming methods and general lifestyle. The most obvious reminders of this civilisation are the pyramids—engineering and architectural marvels—still standing after 4500 years.

Use the report on page 43 to complete the page.

1. Title

Write another suitable title.

2. Classification

List three facts from this section of the report.

3. Description

(a) Give a definition for these terms.

   (i)   Kemet _____

   (ii) Deshret _____

   (iii) hieroglyphics _____

_____

   (iv) pharaoh _____

_____

_____

   (v) afterlife _____

_____

   (vi) mummified _____

_____

(b) Which paragraph in the *description* section discusses Ancient Egyptian ancestry? _____

(c) What is the main idea of paragraph 4 of the *description* section?

_____

_____

(d) Reports are usually written in the present tense, but this historical report has been written mainly in the past tense. Write two examples of where the present tense has been used in paragraph 3 of this section.

_____

_____

(e) (i) These sentences about **Ancient Egypt** have been written in the _____ person. Change them so they are written in the third person.

   (ii) *I was surrounded by natural boundaries that gave me protection from invading armies. This allowed me to grow in my own way, without outside influences.*

_____

_____

4. Conclusion

List two comments the writer makes about pyramids.

• _____

• _____

1. Plan a historical report about another ancient civilisation. Your report will need to be written mainly in the past tense and include vocabulary specific to your subject.

Title

Classification

A general statement about the subject.

Description

Divide the description into sections.

Conclusion

It may contain a personal opinion.

2. Write your report.

3. Edit your work.

Structural and language features are shown on the left and right of the text below.

Title – the headline states what is being reported	**LIFESTYLE WEEKLY** 　　　　　　　　　　　　　　**25 May** **EATING DISORDERS ON THE RISE**	• information is organised into paragraphs
Classification – a subhead or general statement about the subject of the report	Current worldwide surveys reveal eating disorders, particularly in young women, are continuing to increase.	• written in timeless present tense; **contribute**, **are varied**
Description – provides accurate description and facts	An eating disorder is a condition in which a person has problems with his or her eating habits, often due to an obsessive attitude about food and body image. Surveys have shown that the majority of people with eating disorders are adolescent girls and young women, but both sexes and all age groups are at risk. 'Factors that **contribute** to the development of eating disorders **are varied**', says psychologist, Serena Braun. 'A person may have low self-esteem, be depressed or lonely, or be obsessed as a result of the social pressure of peers and advertising that being thin is being 'perfect'. Whatever the reason, serious eating disorders damage body function and can become life-threatening.' (Ms Braun currently treats patients with anorexia nervosa and bulimia at the Royal London Hospital.) **Anorexia** is a complex **psychological disorder** in which people literally starve themselves. It is associated with a distorted body image whereby a severely underweight person thinks he or she is fat. The weight loss is achieved by not eating (or very little food intake), excessive exercise, taking of laxatives or a combination of all three. The harmful effects of anorexia include lowered resistance to illness; dry brittle bones and hair or hair loss; digestive problems such as bloating and constipation; loss of menstrual periods in females; severe dehydration; irregular heartbeat; excessively low blood pressure; anaemia and low body temperature. If untreated, anorexia can be fatal. 'I have **patients** coming to see me looking like skeletons, with protruding bones, legs that look like matchsticks and gaunt, haggard faces, yet **they** are convinced their attitude towards food and their weight is reasonable', says Ms Braun. 'They are usually referred by a concerned parent or relative. They rarely seek help themselves as they don't consider themselves ill. If left untreated, up to 20 per cent of people with this condition die.' Bulimia is the uncontrollable urge to eat large amounts of food in a short time, followed by purging (self-induced vomiting or laxative usage). Bulimics are harder to identify than anorexics because they maintain a more normal weight and attempt to keep their purging a secret. Harmful effects include inflammation of the oesophagus from frequent vomiting, tooth and gum problems, constipation, vitamin and mineral deficiencies and chronic kidney problems. Though bulimia is not as serious as anorexia, fatalities do occur. 'Treatment is a vital step in the recovery of both disorders', says Ms Braun. '**Sixty per cent of people who receive treatment will recover**, but individuals who try to stop on their own nearly always return to the disorder.'	• technical vocabulary and subject-specific terms are used; e.g. **Anorexia**, **psychological disorder** • written in the third person; e.g. **patients**, **they** • uses factual language rather than imaginative; e.g. **Sixty per cent of people who receive treatment will recover**
Conclusion – a final comment about the subject of the report. (It may include an expert or personal opinion or be a summarising comment.)	Family and friends are usually the first to notice someone with one of these disorders. Help is available from a healthcare professional or an eating disorder association. 　　　　　　　　　　　　　　　　　　　　　　Bethany Knight, London	

Teacher information

- Read through the magazine report with the pupils and discuss its features.
- Revise the third person (see page 38). Pupils complete the analysis on page 48.
- Before pupils attempt to plan and write their own report on page 49, model this process with the whole class, using another subject or issue pupils are familiar with. Pupils will need to have gathered information about the issue of their choice prior to planning their report.
- Pupils' reports could be read out orally by them in small groups or to the whole class and discussed. (Purpose/Audience)
- Published reports, accompanied with appropriate illustrations, could be displayed for other pupils to read and compare. (Publishing/Display/Purpose)
- The activity could be done in conjunction with a health topic. Appropriate reports could be published in the school's newsletter to inform other pupils and parents about an issue. (Context/Purpose)

Answers

Page 48
1 Teacher check
2. Teacher check
3. (a) (i)   dehydration
　　　(ii) anaemia
　　　(iii) psychologist
　　　(iv) oesophagus
　　　(v) laxative
　(b) Anorexia **is** a complex psychological disorder in which people literally **starve** themselves. It **is associated** with a distorted body image whereby a severely underweight person **thinks** he or she **is** fat.
　(c) (i)   second person
　　　(ii) Sixty per cent of **people** who receive treatment will recover, but if **they/individuals** try to stop on **their** own **their** disorder will nearly always return. **They** can seek help by contacting **their** local healthcare professional or eating disorder association.
4. Teacher check

Lifestyle Weekly

25 May

EATING DISORDERS ON THE RISE

Current worldwide surveys reveal eating disorders, particularly in young women, are continuing to increase.

An eating disorder is a condition in which a person has problems with his or her eating habits, often due to an obsessive attitude about food and body image. Surveys have shown that the majority of people with eating disorders are adolescent girls and young women, but both sexes and all age groups are at risk.

'Factors that contribute to the development of eating disorders are varied', says psychologist, Serena Braun. 'A person may have low self-esteem, be depressed or lonely, or be obsessed as a result of the social pressure of peers and advertising that being thin is being 'perfect'. Whatever the reason, serious eating disorders damage body function and can become life-threatening.' (Ms Braun currently treats patients with anorexia nervosa and bulimia at the Royal London Hospital.)

Anorexia is a complex psychological disorder in which people literally starve themselves. It is associated with a distorted body image whereby a severely underweight person thinks he or she is fat. The weight loss is achieved by not eating (or very little food intake), excessive exercise, taking of laxatives or a combination of all three. The harmful effects of anorexia include lowered resistance to illness; dry brittle bones and hair or hair loss; digestive problems such as bloating and constipation; loss of menstrual periods in females; severe dehydration; irregular heartbeat; excessively low blood pressure; anaemia and low body temperature. If untreated, anorexia can be fatal.

'I have patients coming to see me looking like skeletons, with protruding bones, legs that look like matchsticks and gaunt, haggard faces, yet they are convinced their attitude towards food and their weight is reasonable', says Ms Braun. 'They are usually referred by a concerned parent or relative. They rarely seek help themselves as they don't consider themselves ill. If left untreated, up to 20 per cent of people with this condition die.'

Bulimia is the uncontrollable urge to eat large amounts of food in a short time, followed by purging (self-induced vomiting or laxative usage). Bulimics are harder to identify than anorexics because they maintain a more normal weight and attempt to keep their purging a secret. Harmful effects include inflammation of the oesophagus from frequent vomiting, tooth and gum problems, constipation, vitamin and mineral deficiencies and chronic kidney problems. Though bulimia is not as serious as anorexia, fatalities do occur.

'Treatment is a vital step in the recovery of both disorders', says Ms Braun. 'Sixty per cent of people who receive treatment will recover, but individuals who try to stop on their own nearly always return to the disorder.'

Family and friends are usually the first to notice someone with one of these disorders. Help is available from a healthcare professional or an eating disorder association.

Bethany Knight, London

Use the report on page 47 to complete the page.

1. Title

Do you think the headline is appropriate? **yes** ☐ **no** ☐

Explain your answer.

_____

_____

_____

2. Classification

Write another suitable subhead.

3. Description

(a) Find a medical term in the report to match each definition.

  (i) a condition where the body is lacking in fluids

  _____

  (ii) a condition where the body has reduced red blood cells

  _____

  (iii) a person who studies how the mind works

  _____

  (iv) the tube connecting the back of the mouth with the stomach

  _____

  (v) a medicine to assist in the easy passing of waste from the body

  _____

(b) Underline the present tense verbs.

Anorexia is a complex psychological disorder in which people literally starve themselves. It is associated with distorted body image whereby a severely underweight person thinks he or she is fat.

(c) Sixty per cent of you who receive treatment will recover, but if you try to stop on your own your disorder will nearly always return. You can seek help by contacting your local healthcare professional or eating disorder association.

  (i) These sentences about people who receive treatment have been written in the _____ person.

  (ii) Change them so they are written in the third person.

4. Conclusion

Write a conclusion that contains a personal opinion about the report.

_____

_____

1. Plan a report for a newspaper or magazine about a health issue. Include accurate facts, subject-specific vocabulary, use the present tense and write in the third person.

Title

A catchy headline.

Classification

A subhead or general statement about the subject of the report.

Description

Divide the description into sections.

Conclusion

It may contain an expert or personal opinion or be a summarising comment.

2. Write your report.

3. Edit your work.

Structural and language features are shown on the left and right of the text below.

Title	**Computer-generated imagery at the cinema**	
Definition – one or more sentences that state what the explanation is about	Computer-generated imagery, or CGI, is a type of animation created by computers. CGI has been used in films such as *Toy story*, *Shrek* and *The Incredibles*. Animation is a way of creating the illusion of movement by showing a sequence of drawings. The trick is to make each drawing slightly different from the one before it.	• subject-specific vocabulary; **animation**, **storyboards**
Description – information presented in logical order	Making a CGI film begins with a story idea, which is explained or 'pitched' to the **animation** team. Once the initial script and action is decided upon, **storyboards** of the film are drawn. These are like rough cartoon strips. The artists drawing the storyboards must take into account the lines in the script and the movements and emotions that need to be shown by the characters in the film. **Once** the storyboards are ready, 'scratch' or rough voices are recorded to go with the storyboards. **At this stage**, these are not done by actors—they are usually recorded by the artists or other people in the team. The storyboards and voices are put together to make a videotape and the team can get its first glimpse of what the film might look like. Next, the characters, sets and props are designed. Sometimes, actual models of these are made by hand and then scanned into a computer. Alternatively, three-dimensional images are drawn straight into the computer. The computer image of a character is called a 'wireframe model'. Each wireframe model is given 'avars'— hinges that allow the animator to move parts of the character, like its arms or jaw. A character may have up to 100 avars just for the face! Once the characters, sets and props are ready, animation software is used to choreograph each scene of the film with movements and facial expressions. Other software is also used to add colour and texture to make the film look more realistic; for example, to create the look of fur or skin. Finally, the scenes are digitally lit—just like using actual lights on a normal film! The lighting effects are used to enhance the mood of each scene. The last step in creating a CGI film **is called** 'rendering'. A computer **produces** a two-dimensional frame of film from each animated shot that has been created. This process may take many weeks. Final touches such as sound effects and music can then be added.	• linking words to show cause and effect; e.g. **Once**, **At this stage** • majority of verbs in the present tense; e.g. **is called**, **produces** • information is organised into paragraphs
Conclusion – an evaluation or interesting comment	CGI films have only been around since the 1990s, so they can be considered very new technology. Most people think these films look extremely realistic now—who knows what they may look like in another decade?	

Teacher information

- Explanations usually outline how something occurs, works or is made. This particular explanation shows how something is made.
- Before pupils read the text independently, discuss the imagery in films such as *Toy story*, *Shrek* and *The Incredibles*. Once the text is read, ask selected pupils to explain the steps involved in making CGI films.
- Identify and discuss the structural features indicated above and ask pupils to identify specific examples of the language features.
- Pupils should then complete the analysis on page 52.
- Model the planning and writing of an explanation using the framework on page 53. Pupils may wish to suggest a suitable topic; e.g. how a toaster or vacuum cleaner works. The pupils can then follow this example to plan and write their own explanation about how something works.
- Pupils may need to use the library, the Internet or other resources to research information to plan their explanation.
- Pupils could publish their explanations and add diagrams, illustrations or three-dimensional models for display. (Publishing/Display/Purpose)
- The pupils' explanations could be given as an oral presentation to small groups or the whole class. An actual model could be used where appropriate, to assist in the explanation. (Purpose/Audience/Context)
- Published explanations could be displayed for other pupils to read and compare, especially those who chose the same subject. (Publishing/Display)

Answers

Page 52

1. Teacher check

2. (a) CGI stands for computer-generated imagery, a type of animation created by computers.

   (b) Animation is a way of creating the illusion of movement by showing a series of drawings.

3. (a) (i) rough, strips
      (ii) wireframe model
      (iii) hinge, move

   (b) Next, Sometimes, Alternatively, and

   (c) (i) begins, is pitched
       (ii) are, are recorded

   (d) Teacher check

   (e) Teacher check

4. Teacher check

Computer-generated imagery at the cinema

Computer-generated imagery, or CGI, is a type of animation created by computers. CGI has been used in films such as *Toy story*, *Shrek* and *The Incredibles*. Animation is a way of creating the illusion of movement by showing a sequence of drawings. The trick is to make each drawing slightly different from the one before it.

Making a CGI film begins with a story idea, which is explained or 'pitched' to the animation team. Once the initial script and action is decided upon, storyboards of the film are drawn. These are like rough cartoon strips. The artists drawing the storyboards must take into account the lines in the script and the movements and emotions that need to be shown by the characters in the film.

Once the storyboards are ready, 'scratch' or rough voices are recorded to go with the storyboards. At this stage, these are not done by actors—they are usually recorded by the artists or other people in the team. The storyboards and voices are put together to make a videotape and the team can get its first glimpse of what the film might look like.

Next, the characters, sets and props are designed. Sometimes, actual models of these are made by hand and then scanned into a computer. Alternatively, three-dimensional images are drawn straight into the computer. The computer image of a character is called a 'wireframe model'. Each wireframe model is given 'avars'—hinges that allow the animator to move parts of the character, like its arms or jaw. A character may have up to 100 avars just for the face!

Once the characters, sets and props are ready, animation software is used to choreograph each scene of the film with movements and facial expressions. Other software is also used to add colour and texture to make the film look more realistic; for example, to create the look of fur or skin. Finally, the scenes are digitally lit—just like using actual lights on a normal film! The lighting effects are used to enhance the mood of each scene.

The last step in creating a CGI film is called 'rendering'. A computer produces a two-dimensional frame of film from each animated shot that has been created. This process may take many weeks. Final touches such as sound effects and music can then be added.

CGI films have only been around since the 1990s, so they can be considered very new technology. Most people think these films look extremely realistic now—who knows what they may look like in another decade?

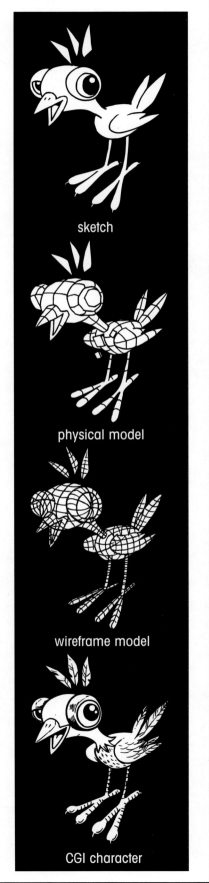

sketch

physical model

wireframe model

CGI character

Use the report on page 51 to complete the page.

1. Title

(a) Is the title appropriate?

yes ☐   no ☐

(b) Explain your answer.

2. Definition

(a) What is CGI?

_____

_____

_____

(b) What is animation?

_____

_____

_____

3. Description

(a) Fill in the missing words to explain the meaning of these terms.

(i)   Storyboards for CGI films are like _____ cartoon _____.

(ii) The computer image of a CGI character is called a _____.

(iii) An avar is a _____ that allows an animator to _____ parts of a character.

(b) List three examples of linking words from paragraph 3 of the description section.

(c) Highlight the present tense verbs in these sentences.

(i) A CGI film begins with a story idea, which is pitched to the animation team.

(ii) Once the storyboards are ready, scratch voices are recorded to go with them.

(d) Do you think the illustration helps to explain how CGI films are made? **yes** ☐ **no** ☐

(e) Why are illustrations or diagrams important in explanations?

_____

_____

4. Conclusion

(a) List two comments the writer makes in the conclusion.

• _____

• _____

(b) Write a new conclusion for this text that contains a different interesting comment.

_____

_____

1. Plan an explanation about how something works.

Title

Definition

Description

Conclusion

2. Write your explanation.

3. Edit your work.

Structural and language features are shown on the left and right of the text below.

Title	**April Fools' Day**	• subject-specific vocabulary; **sixteenth century**, **Julian calendar**
Definition – one or more sentences that state what the explanation is about	April Fools' Day, an occasion celebrated on 1 April every year, is a day when people play jokes or tricks on each other.	
Description – information presented in logical order	No-one is absolutely sure how this tradition came about, but evidence seems to suggest that it first began in France in the **sixteenth century**. At this time, the French did not use the same calendar we use today. On their calendar (the **Julian calendar**), New Year's Day did not fall on 1 January but on 25 March. This marked the beginning of spring and the religious observance of the Feast of the Annunciation. But much of the actual celebrating for New Year's Day—parties, special meals and dancing late into the night—generally took place on 1 April. Some historians say this was because 25 March often clashed with Easter. Others say that New Year was marked with a week-long celebration of gift-giving and parties, the final day of which fell on 1 April. During this medieval era, much of Europe celebrated New Year in the same way.	• linking words to show cause and effect; e.g. **However**, **As a result**
	However, in 1582, Pope Gregory XIII introduced the Gregorian calendar, which among other things meant moving New Year's Day from the end of March to 1 January. France was one of the first countries to adopt this calendar—the one in use today. When the king of France, King Charles IX, proclaimed that New Year's Day would now be moved to 1 January, many French people refused to accept the change, did not hear about it or did not believe it. **As a result**, they continued to celebrate New Year on 1 April.	• this explanation is about a historical subject so the past as well as the present tense is used; e.g. **was fooled**, **is called**
	Consequently, these people often became the butt of jokes. Those who wanted to make fun of them would pay them mock visits on 1 April, give funny gifts, send invitations to parties that were never to take place or send them on 'fools' errands'! Any person who **was fooled** in these ways was called a 'poisson d'avril' or 'April fish'. This may have been because the person was acting like a young, inexperienced fish—easily caught on a hook! Another reason was that the sun was leaving the zodiacal sign of Pisces, the fish, at this time of the year. Eventually, the French got used to the new date for New Year's Day, but the custom of prank-playing on 1 April continued. In France today, April 1 **is called** 'Poisson d'avril' and French children sometimes attach a paper fish on a friend's back. When the prank is discovered, the friend is called 'Poisson d'avril'.	
	Gradually, the tradition moved to other countries after they adopted the Gregorian calendar. Some countries took a long time to change—1660 in Scotland, and 1700 in Denmark, Norway and Germany. However, it would take almost two hundred years for the tradition to be taken up by the English in 1752. They called it 'All Fools' Day' or 'April Fools' Day', as we know it today. Traditionally, jokes are played only up to midday—otherwise the victim can call the joker the fool!	• information is organised into paragraphs
Conclusion – an evaluation or interesting comment	Today, practical joke playing on 1 April is a common practice all over the world. However, it is important to remember that the jokes and pranks people play on each other should be all in good fun—for both sides!	

Teacher information

- Explanations usually outline how something occurs, works or is made. This particular explanation shows how something occurred.
- Allow the pupils to read the text independently. Once the text is read, ask selected pupils to explain facts about the origin of April Fools' Day.
- Identify and discuss the structural features indicated above and ask pupils to identify specific examples of the language features. Discuss with the pupils how explanations are generally written in the present tense, but because this explanation is about how an event occurred, the past tense is used.
- Pupils should then complete the analysis on page 56.
- Model the planning and writing of an explanation using the framework on page 57. Pupils may wish to suggest a suitable topic; e.g. how Remembrance Day came about. The pupils can then follow this example to plan and write their explanation about how another event, such as Valentine's Day or Thanksgiving in America, originated.
- Pupils will need to use library, the Internet or other resources to research information to plan their explanation.

- The pupils' explanations could be given as an oral presentation to small groups or the whole class during history lessons and discussed. (Purpose/Audience/Context)
- Published explanations could be displayed for other pupils to read and compare, especially those who chose the same event. (Publishing/Display/Purpose)

Answers

Page 56

1–2. Teacher check

3. (a) Teacher check

   (b) Some examples may include: At this time, however, eventually, consequently, gradually.

   (c) (i) past tense – began, proclaimed, wanted, moved, refused, was acting

   (ii) present tense – is called, pay, attach

   (d) The answer should indicate that the writer uses these phrases as no-one is absolutely sure of how the tradition began.

4. (a) • Joke playing on April Fools' Day is common practice worldwide.

   • The jokes should all be in good fun for both sides.

   (b) Teacher check

April Fools' Day

April Fools' Day, an occasion celebrated on 1 April every year, is a day when people play jokes or tricks on each other.

No-one is absolutely sure how this tradition came about, but evidence seems to suggest that it first began in France in the sixteenth century. At this time, the French did not use the same calendar we use today. On their calendar (the Julian calendar), New Year's Day did not fall on 1 January but on 25 March. This marked the beginning of spring and the religious observance of the Feast of the Annunciation. But much of the actual celebrating for New Year's Day—parties, special meals and dancing late into the night—generally took place on 1 April. Some historians say this was because 25 March often clashed with Easter. Others say that New Year was marked with a week-long celebration of gift-giving and parties, the final day of which fell on 1 April. During this medieval era, much of Europe celebrated New Year in the same way.

However, in 1582, Pope Gregory XIII introduced the Gregorian calendar, which among other things meant moving New Year's Day from the end of March to 1 January. France was one of the first countries to adopt this calendar—the one in use today. When the king of France, King Charles IX, proclaimed that New Year's Day would now be moved to 1 January, many French people refused to accept the change, did not hear about it or did not believe it. As a result, they continued to celebrate New Year on 1 April.

Consequently, these people often became the butt of jokes. Those who wanted to make fun of them would pay them mock visits on 1 April, give funny gifts, send invitations to parties that were never to take place or send them on 'fools' errands'! Any person who was fooled in these ways was called a 'poisson d'avril' or 'April fish'. This may have been because the person was acting like a young, inexperienced fish—easily caught on a hook! Another reason was that the sun was leaving the zodiacal sign of Pisces, the fish, at this time of the year. Eventually, the French got used to the new date for New Year's Day, but the custom of prank-playing on April 1 continued. In France today, 1 April is called 'Poisson d'avril' and French children sometimes attach a paper fish on a friend's back. When the prank is discovered, the friend is called 'Poisson d'avril'.

Gradually, the tradition moved to other countries after they adopted the Gregorian calendar. Some countries took a long time to change—1660 in Scotland, and 1700 in Denmark, Norway and Germany. However, it would take almost two hundred years for the tradition to be taken up by the English in 1752. They called it 'All Fools' Day' or 'April Fools' Day', as we know it today. Traditionally, jokes are played only up to midday—otherwise the victim can call the joker the fool!

Today, practical joke playing on 1 April is a common practice all over the world. However, it is important to remember that the jokes and pranks people play on each other should be all in good fun—for both sides!

I am a slimy slug!

Use the report on page 55 to complete the page.

1. Title

(a) Is the title, 'April Fools' Day' a suitable one for this explanation?   **yes** ☐ **no** ☐

(b) Why?/Why not? _____

_____

_____

_____

2. Definition

List two facts from this section.

_____

_____

3. Description

(a) List four examples of subject-specific vocabulary from the description section.

_____

_____

_____

(b) Write three examples of linking words from paragraph 1 of this section.

_____

(c) As this explanation is about how an event occurred, the past tense is used as well as the present tense. Sort these verbs from the text into past and present tense.

began   proclaimed   wanted   is called   moved   refused   pay   was acting   attach

(i) past tense	(ii) present tense

(d) Why does the writer use phrases such as 'evidence seems to suggest', and 'some historians say' when trying to explain facts about the origin of April Fools' Day?

_____

_____

4. Conclusion

(a) What two comments does the writer make in the conclusion?

• _____

• _____

(b) Write a new conclusion for this text that contains a different interesting comment.

_____

_____

1. Plan an explanation about the history of an event we now celebrate. You will need to write most of the text in the past tense.

Title

Definition

Description

Conclusion

2. Write your explanation.

3. Edit your work.

Structural and language features are shown on the left and right of the text below.

Title	**Glass**
Definition – one or more sentences that state what the explanation is about	Glass is a hard, normally transparent substance. The main ingredient of glass is sand. Glass is used to make a huge number of products, including windows, spectacle lenses, ornaments, mirrors, light bulbs and computer screens.
Description – information presented in logical order	To begin making glass, raw materials are mixed in a vat in a special factory. These materials are usually silica sand (silicon dioxide), soda ash (sodium carbonate) and limestone (calcium carbonate). Special kinds of glass such as **heat-resistant** ovenware are made by including boric oxide in the ingredients. Lead glass, which sparkles brilliantly when cut, has **potash** and red lead added. Recycled or waste glass can also be used as a raw material. It is called 'cullet'. Sometimes, new glass can be made entirely from cullet.
	Once mixed, the raw materials are heated in a furnace to an extremely high temperature—about 1500 °C! This is about 40 times hotter than the hottest summer's day. Once at this temperature, the raw materials melt and form a liquid or 'molten glass'. The interesting thing about molten glass is that it does not behave like most other liquids as it cools. Instead of forming crystals, like water does when it turns into ice, it keeps a toffee-like consistency. So while it is still hot, it can be moulded into different shapes and will stay in that shape when it hits room temperature.
	Depending on what the glass is to be made into, there are different ways of **shaping** the molten glass. One of these is called glass blowing. This is a very old method of shaping glass. It is done by a person blowing into an iron pipe which has been dipped into the molten glass. When the person blows into the pipe, the glass **forms** a bubble which can then be stretched and cut into different shapes. High quality glassware and specially shaped glass containers needed in chemical laboratories are hand blown by skilled glass-blowers using this method. Other ways of shaping glass include 'drawing' (using air pressure or gravity to draw molten glass over a hollow cylinder or cone until it becomes rigid to make tubing, rod, or sheet glass) and 'pressing' (pouring hot glass into moulds to make a variety of products from glass bottles to sealed beam headlight lenses).
	Once most molten glass has been shaped, it is strengthened by reheating it and cooling it down again slowly. This is called 'annealing'. Some glass products also go through a process called 'tempering'. This is when the glass is reheated and then cooled suddenly, making it even stronger than glass which has only been annealed.
	Finally, the finished glass is decorated if necessary. Methods of decoration include cutting, copper-wheel engraving, etching with hydrofluoric acid, gilding, enamelling and painting. **Then** it is inspected and packaged and can leave the factory from where it finds its way to you!
Conclusion – an evaluation or interesting comment	Think about the number of different glass products we encounter in one day. Glass is an extremely versatile product and unlike many other manufactured substances, it does not rust or react to many chemicals.

Right-hand margin notes:
- subject-specific vocabulary; **heat-resistant**, **potash**
- majority of verbs in the present tense; e.g. **shaping**, **forms**
- linking words to show cause and effect; e.g. **Finally**, **then**
- information is organised into paragraphs

Teacher information

- Explanations usually outline how something occurs, works or is made. This particular explanation shows how something is made.
- Allow the pupils to read the text independently. Once the text is read, ask selected pupils to explain the steps involved in making glass.
- Identify and discuss the structural features indicated above and ask pupils to identify specific examples of the language features.
- Pupils should then complete the analysis on page 60.
- Model the planning and writing of an explanation using the framework on page 61. Pupils may wish to suggest a suitable topic; e.g. how milk is made or how gold is extracted. The pupils can then follow this example to plan and write their own explanation about how something is made.
- Pupils may need to use the library, the Internet or other resources to research information to plan their explanation.
- The pupils' explanations could be given as an oral presentation to small groups or the whole class as part of a science or technology lesson and discussed. (Purpose/Audience/Context)
- Published explanations, along with appropriate illustrations or diagrams, could be displayed for other pupils to read and compare, especially those who chose the same subject. (Publishing/Display/Purpose)

Answers

Page 60
1. Teacher check
2. (a) Glass is a hard, normally transparent substance.
   (b) sand
   (c) Teacher check
3. (a) (i) calcium carbonate
       (ii) cullet
       (iii) annealing
       (iv) tempering
       (v) pressing
   (b) then, to begin, finally, while, once, sometimes, when, instead of
   (c) (i) The raw materials are mixed in a vat and are heated in a furnace.
       (ii) When the person blows into the pipe, the glass forms a bubble which is stretched and cut into different shapes.
4. (a) (iii)
   (b) Teacher check

Glass

Glass is a hard, normally transparent substance. The main ingredient of glass is sand. Glass is used to make a huge number of products, including windows, spectacle lenses, ornaments, mirrors, light bulbs and computer screens.

To begin making glass, raw materials are mixed in a vat in a special factory. These materials are usually silica sand (silicon dioxide), soda ash (sodium carbonate) and limestone (calcium carbonate). Special kinds of glass such as heat-resistant ovenware are made by including boric oxide in the ingredients. Lead glass, which sparkles brilliantly when cut, has potash and red lead added. Recycled or waste glass can also be used as a raw material. It is called 'cullet'. Sometimes, new glass can be made entirely from cullet.

Once mixed, the raw materials are heated in a furnace to an extremely high temperature—about 1500 °C! This is about 40 times hotter than the hottest summer's day. Once at this temperature, the raw materials melt and form a liquid or 'molten glass'. The interesting thing about molten glass is that it does not behave like most other liquids as it cools. Instead of forming crystals, like water does when it turns into ice, it keeps a toffee-like consistency. So while it is still hot, it can be moulded into different shapes and will stay in that shape when it hits room temperature.

Depending on what the glass is to be made into, there are different ways of shaping the molten glass. One of these is called glass blowing. This is a very old method of shaping glass. It is done by a person blowing into an iron pipe which has been dipped into the molten glass. When the person blows into the pipe, the glass forms a bubble which can then be stretched and cut into different shapes. High quality glassware and specially shaped glass containers needed in chemical laboratories are hand blown by skilled glass-blowers using this method. Other ways of shaping glass include 'drawing' (using air pressure or gravity to draw molten glass over a hollow cylinder or cone until it becomes rigid to make tubing, rod, or sheet glass) and 'pressing' (pouring hot glass into moulds to make a variety of products from glass bottles to sealed beam headlight lenses).

Once most molten glass has been shaped, it is strengthened by reheating it and cooling it down again slowly. This is called 'annealing'. Some glass products also go through a process called 'tempering'. This is when the glass is reheated and then cooled suddenly, making it even stronger than glass which has only been annealed.

Finally, the finished glass is decorated if necessary. Methods of decoration include cutting, copper-wheel engraving, etching with hydrofluoric acid, gilding, enamelling and painting. Then it is inspected and packaged and can leave the factory from where it finds its way to you!

Think about the number of different glass products we encounter in one day. Glass is an extremely versatile product and unlike many other manufactured substances, it does not rust or react to many chemicals.

Use the report on page 59 to complete the page.

1. Title

What are some features of an appropriate title for an explanation?

_____

2. Definition

(a) What is glass?

_____

(b) What is its main ingredient?

_____

3. Description

(a) Find the technical term in the text for these definitions.

(i) limestone

_____

(ii) recycled or waste glass used in glass making

_____

(iii) strengthening glass by reheating and slowly cooling it

_____

(iv) strengthening glass by reheating and suddenly cooling it

_____

(v) pouring hot glass into moulds

_____

(b) Which of these words are used in the text to link ideas or show cause and effect?

then   to begin   finally   methods

while   once   decorated   sometimes

when   special   instead of

(c) Change these sentences from the past tense to the present tense.

(i) The raw materials were mixed in a vat and were heated in a furnace.

(ii) When the person blew into the pipe, the glass formed a bubble which was stretched and cut into different shapes.

4. Conclusion

(a) Tick one box.

(i) The writer has made an evaluative comment. ☐

(ii) The writer has made an interesting comment. ☐

(iii) The writer has made an evaluative and an interesting comment. ☐

(b) Write a conclusion which includes both a comment and an evaluation.

_____

_____

_____

_____

_____

1. Plan an explanation about how something is made.

Title

Definition

Description

Conclusion

2. Write your explanation.

3. Edit your work.

Structural and language features are shown on the left and right of the text below.

Title	**Real people**	
Introduction – one or more sentences that state the problem and the writer's position	It always amazes me how advertisers on television and in magazines are always using '**stick-thin**', '**perfect-looking**' models to sell their products! These models always have the best clothes, the nicest cars, perfect skin, perfect hair and bodies, are popular with everyone and go to the best parties. Real people are not like that! More 'real' people **should** be used in advertisements!	• a variety of controlling and emotive words; '**stick-thin**', '**perfect-looking**, **should**
Arguments – presented in logical manner with supporting details, usually from strongest to weakest	If advertisers used more 'real' people, the public would be able to relate to the advertisements better! 'Real' people come in all shapes and sizes. They have 'good hair days' and 'bad hair days'. They get rashes, acne, cold sores and scabs on their knees. They can't afford to ride around in fancy cars and go to parties with all the 'right' people. They can't afford to wear the most fashionable clothes all the time. 'Real' people are more interesting, approachable and 'normal'.	• paragraphs used to state and elaborate on each point
	When some people see 'perfect' models on television and in magazines, they think that they should look like that too! It gives them an unrealistic view of things! It can make them feel unhappy with their own appearance. They think they are too fat or their hair is wrong or their face is not pretty enough! They may think that they wear the wrong clothes or their body is wrong! They don't think they are good enough because all they see on the television and in magazines are 'perfect' people! This can give them a poor opinion of themselves. Using 'real' people in advertisements would help everyone realise that they are good enough just as they are! They would not feel bad about themselves!	• a variety of conjunctions; e.g. **if**, **because**
	Another reason why 'real' people should be used in advertisements is so that people seeing the advertisements will eat and exercise in a healthy way. Quite often, people who want to look like the models in advertisements diet to make themselves thin or go on unhealthy 'crash' diets or even develop eating disorders such as anorexia nervosa or bulimia. They can even exercise too much to make themselves thinner! 'Real' people have a sensible diet and are not obsessive about exercising all the time! Using 'real' people in advertisements won't contribute to eating disorders and other health problems!	• persuasive language is used so others will agree with the writers point of view; e.g. **only sensible**, **Get real**
	Have you ever noticed how people in advertisements have lots of fashionable clothes, fancy cars or jewellery? Advertisements with people like this can make viewers want things they don't need. They can become dissatisfied with what they have and want more and more 'things'. The advertisements also make you think that you will be the most popular person at school and have a great social life **if** you only buy the things they want you to buy! Using 'real' people will stop others from being dissatisfied with what they have!	
Conclusion – restates the writer's position and summarises arguments	I think it is **only sensible** to use 'real' people in advertisements **because** everyone can identify with them. People would make the best of their own appearance and not want to look like someone else. Young adults would not get eating disorders or want to have lots of material possessions that they don't need! **Get 'real'**, advertisers, and use 'real' people!	

Teacher information

- Discussions argue for a particular position and attempt to persuade an audience to share this view.
- Pupils should read the discussion independently.
- Identify the structural and language features indicated above before the pupils complete the analysis on page 64. Ask pupils to identify examples of controlling and emotive words and conjunctions in the text.
- Teachers should hold a class discussion on some appropriate issues the pupils could write discussions about. Make a list of topics for later use.
- Select one of these suggestions to model the planning and writing of a discussion, using the framework on page 65. The pupils can then follow this example to plan and write their discussions about 'takeaway food'.
- Pupils could display their discussion with a colourful illustration of their favourite 'healthy takeaway food'. (Display)
- Pupils write discussions about issues mentioned in Heath and values lessons. (Context)
- Pupils may give their discussions as oral presentations to other members of the class about an issue of concern. (Purpose/Audience)
- Pupils use their discussions to encourage pupils in a younger class to make healthier choices when selecting 'junk food'. (Context/Audience)

Answers

Page 64
1. Teacher check
2. Teacher check
3. (a) (i) People would relate to advertisements better if 'real' people were used.
   (ii) Advertisements with 'perfect' people in them make 'real' people feel bad about themselves.
   (iii) Advertisers who use 'perfect' models encourage viewers to go on 'crash' diets that contribute to health problems.
   (iv) Some advertisements encourage people to want more 'things'.
(b) – (c) Teacher check
4. Teacher check

Real people

It always amazes me how advertisers on television and in magazines are always using 'stick-thin', 'perfect-looking' models to sell their products! These models always have the best clothes, the nicest cars, perfect skin, perfect hair and bodies, are popular with everyone and go to the best parties. Real people are not like that! More 'real' people should be used in advertisements!

If advertisers used more 'real' people, the public would be able to relate to the advertisements better! 'Real' people come in all shapes and sizes. They have 'good hair days' and 'bad hair days'. They get rashes, acne, cold sores and scabs on their knees. They can't afford to ride around in fancy cars and go to parties with all the 'right' people. They can't afford to wear the most fashionable clothes all the time. Real people are more interesting, approachable and 'normal'.

When some people see 'perfect' models on television and in magazines, they think that they should look like that too! It gives them an unrealistic view of things! It can make them feel unhappy with their own appearance. They think they are too fat or their hair is wrong or their face is not pretty enough! They may think that they wear the wrong clothes or their body is wrong! They don't think they are good enough because all they see on the television and in magazines are 'perfect' people! This can give them a poor opinion of themselves. Using 'real' people in advertisements would help everyone realise that they are good enough just as they are! They would not feel bad about themselves!

Another reason why 'real' people should be used in advertisements is so that people seeing the advertisements will eat and exercise in a healthy way. Quite often, people who want to look like the models in advertisements diet to make themselves thin or go on unhealthy 'crash' diets or even develop eating disorders such as anorexia nervosa or bulimia. They can even exercise too much to make themselves thinner! 'Real' people have a sensible diet and are not obsessive about exercising all the time! Using 'real' people in advertisements won't contribute to eating disorders and other health problems!

Have you ever noticed how people in advertisements have lots of fashionable clothes, fancy cars or jewellery? Advertisements with people like this can make viewers want things they don't need. They can become dissatisfied with what they have and want more and more 'things'. The advertisements also make you think that you will be the most popular person at school and have a great social life if you only buy the things they want you to buy! Using 'real' people will stop others from being dissatisfied with what they have!

I think it is only sensible to use 'real' people in advertisements because everyone can identify with them. People would make the best of their own appearance and not want to look like someone else. Young adults would not get eating disorders or want to have lots of material possessions that they don't need! Get 'real', advertisers, and use 'real' people!

Use the discussion on page 63 to complete the page.

1. Title

Write another title which is
interesting and appropriate.

2. Introduction

In your own words, state the problem and the writer's point of view.

_____

_____

3. Arguments

(a) Write a summary of the argument in each
paragraph of this section.

(i) _____

_____

_____

_____

(ii) _____

_____

_____

_____

(iii) _____

_____

_____

_____

(iv) _____

_____

_____

_____

(b) The argument in the first paragraph of this
section may not be the strongest in your opinion.
Number the paragraphs in order from the
strongest to the weakest arguments.

Paragraph 1 ☐

Paragraph 2 ☐

Paragraph 3 ☐

Paragraph 4 ☐

(c) Write two examples of each of the following
language features:

(i) controlling or emotive words

```



```

(ii) conjunctions

```



```

4. Conclusion

(a) Tick the boxes.

(i) The arguments are summarised ☐   (ii) An evaluative comment is given. ☐

(b) Write a new evaluative comment for the conclusion, restating the writer's point of view.

_____

_____

1. Plan a discussion telling how 'takeaway' food is not always a bad thing.

Title

Introduction

State the issue and your point of view.

Arguments

List each argument you will use, giving the strongest one first.

Conclusion

End by restating your point of view and summarising your arguments.

2. Write your discussion.   **3.** Edit your work.

Structural and language features are shown on the left and right of the text below.

Title	**Letter to the editor**	
Introduction – one or more sentences that state the problem and the writer's position	To the editor of 'Television today', I am writing this letter to complain about the number of advertisements aired during the screening of some television programmes. I don't think it's necessary to have so many advertisements during the show. It **would be much better** to watch them at the end of a programme before the next one starts.	• a variety of controlling and emotive words; **would be much better**, **up in the air**
Arguments – presented in logical manner with supporting details, usually from strongest to weakest	Last Friday night, I was watching a really interesting show and it was just getting to one of the best parts of the story when the programme stopped and an advertisement came on! We were left '**up in the air**'. When it came back on again, all the suspense had gone and we had to 'get back into' the story again! Advertisements interrupt the storyline of a programme.	• paragraphs used to state and elaborate on each point
	On the weekend, I was finally able to view a programme I had been waiting for ages to see. I had all my jobs and homework done so that I could enjoy watching without being nagged by Mum to do stuff! If no advertisements were aired in the middle of a show, programmes would finish faster and viewers would stop watching when the actual show was over! Viewers would then have time to exercise more or do their homework or socialise with their friends.	• a variety of conjunctions; e.g. **If**, **which**
	All the advertisements were about computer games, music or fashionable clothes. There were just as many advertisements encouraging people to eat junk food. Advertisements try to persuade people to own more things and be unhealthy. **If** the advertisements for these things were not shown during popular programmes, people would not be made to feel like they have to buy them!	• persuasive language is used so others will agree with the writer's point of view; e.g. **Join me**, **register your complaint**
	Another reason for putting advertisements at the end of a programme, instead of during the programme, is that it makes it so much later before you actually get to bed. Some parents make their children go to bed at a certain time. If advertisements were shown at the end, children could watch all of a good programme and still get a good night's sleep!	
Conclusion – restates the writer's position and summarises arguments	**Join me** and **register your complaint** about this terrible state of affairs **which** is affecting all television viewers. A change is urgently needed so that we can all enjoy television more, stop buying things we really don't need and have much healthier, happier lives. From Lucy Curl	

Teacher information

- Discussions argue for a particular position and attempt to persuade an audience to share this view.
- Pupils should read the discussion independently.
- Identify the structural and language features indicated above before the pupils complete the analysis on page 68. Ask pupils to identify examples of controlling and emotive words and conjunctions in the text.
- Teachers should hold a class discussion on some appropriate issues the pupils could write discussions about. Make a list of topics for later use.
- Select one of these suggestions to model the planning and writing of a discussion using the framework on page 69. The pupils can then follow this example to plan and write their discussions about a change they would like to see in their television programming. Possible topics may include the times certain programmes are aired, the rating of programmes etc.
- Pupils could display their completed discussion inside a television shape, with illustrations of favourite television characters around. (Display)
- Pupils write discussions about issues which may arise during discussions about the media. (Context)
- Pupils may give their discussions about an issue of interest as oral presentations to other members of the class. (Purpose/Audience)
- Pupils use their discussions to encourage pupils in another class to think more about their own television viewing. (Context/Audience)

Answers

Page 68
1. Teacher check
2. The are too many advertisements on television between programmes which she thinks should be shown at the end of programmes.
3. (a) Advertisements interrupt the storyline of programmes.
   (b) Advertisements at the end of programmes would let children get to bed on time.
   (c) – (d) Teacher check
   (e) Answers will vary but may include 'don't think it's necessary', 'left up in the air', 'get back into the story', 'nagged by Mum', 'have to buy them' etc.
4. Teacher check

Letter to the editor

To the editor of 'Television today',

I am writing this letter to complain about the number of advertisements aired during the screening of some television programmes. I don't think it's necessary to have so many advertisements during the show. It would be much better to watch them at the end of a programme before the next one starts.

Last Friday night, I was watching a really interesting show and it was just getting to one of the best parts of the story when the programme stopped and an advertisement came on! We were left 'up in the air'. When it came back on again, all the suspense had gone and we had to 'get back into' the story again! Advertisements interrupt the storyline of a programme.

On the weekend, I was finally able to view a programme I had been waiting for ages to see. I had all my jobs and homework done so that I could enjoy watching without being nagged by Mum to do stuff! If no advertisements were aired in the middle of a show, programmes would finish faster and viewers would stop watching when the actual show was over! Viewers would then have time to exercise more or do their homework or socialise with their friends.

All the advertisements were about computer games, music or fashionable clothes. There were just as many advertisements encouraging people to eat junk food. Advertisements try to persuade people to own more things and be unhealthy. If the advertisements for these things were not shown during popular programmes, people would not be made to feel like they have to buy them!

Another reason for putting advertisements at the end of a programme, instead of during the programme, is that it makes it so much later before you actually get to bed. Some parents make their children go to bed at a certain time. If advertisements were shown at the end, children could watch all of a good programme and still get a good night's sleep!

Join me and register your complaint about this terrible state of affairs which is affecting all television viewers. A change is urgently needed so that we can all enjoy television more, stop buying things we really don't need and have much healthier, happier lives.

From Lucy Curl

Use the discussion on page 67 to complete the page.

1. Title

Write a different, appropriate title.

2. Introduction

What is the issue and what does the writer want done?

_____

_____

3. Arguments

(a) Which argument did the writer start with?

_____

_____

_____

_____

(b) Which argument did the writer make last?

_____

_____

_____

_____

(c) Do you agree with the order of the arguments given?   **yes** ☐ **no** ☐

(d) If your answer is 'no', write the order you think is better below. If you agree with the order, write another argument which could have been included.

_____

_____

(e) Use the box below to write some persuasive words or phrases from the text.

4. Conclusion

Write a new conclusion for the discussion.

_____

_____

_____

_____

1. Plan a discussion about a change you would like to see in your television programming.

Title

Introduction

Arguments

Conclusion

2. Write your discussion.

3. Edit your work.

Structural and language features are shown on the left and right of the text below.

Title	**Stupendous clothing**
Introduction – one or more sentences that state the problem and the writer's position	Gals and guys! Are you the outdoors type — an active person who loves the fresh air and sunshine? Do you live for the sun, sand and surf but are conscious of the dangers of too much exposure to the sun? Do you love spending time in the great outdoors, soaking up the natural beauty of the world around you? Then you **must** not miss this! Our product is created especially to help you enjoy life in the sun but prevent the **deadly damage** it can cause! *Stupendous Industries* has just released its brand new, innovative range of clothing!
Arguments – presented in logical manner with supporting details, usually from strongest to weakest	This extensive range of clothing has been created from exhaustively researched, designed and trialled material. This revolutionary material is guaranteed to resist UV rays, allowing the wearers to spend as much time in the sun as they wish without suffering any damage from these harmful rays. Years of research at the prestigious Yalumbi Institute have finally resulted in the development of this lifestyle-changing product! Imagine being able to spend all weekend in the sun without any skin damage! How practical it is as well for people who spend most of their working lives outside! Landscapers, bricklayers, road workers—all will benefit from wearing clothing made from *Stupenda cloth*™! Employers will want to purchase clothing in this range to protect ALL their workers!
	Not only is *Stupendous clothing* UV resistant, but it may also be fashioned into any type of clothing imaginable! Shirts, trousers, hats, jackets, skirts and dresses are all available in Stupenda cloth™. It is available in every conceivable colour of the rainbow— particularly the most fashionable colours of the year—jade, aqua and peach! What a bonus! Imagine a whole wardrobe of clothing in fashionable, easy-care, colour-coordinated, protective material!
	Stupendous Industries makes its clothing range to fit all sizes. **So** now mothers can protect their children **and** wear equally protective clothing in fashionable designs and colours themselves! What a cost-saver! Fashionable and good for your skin! The whole family will benefit from wearing clothing selected from the *Stupendous clothing* range made from *Stupenda cloth*!
	Stupendous Industries is also soon to release an exclusive range for that easily forgotten member of the family—the family pet! Soon your beloved feline or canine could be adorned in kitty coats and hats or doggy shades and jackets and be protected from sun exposure! This exclusive range will only be available through email order.
Conclusion – restates the writer's position and summarises arguments	**Don't delay**! Find your nearest stockist and purchase your choice of *Stupendous Industries* clothing today! **You won't be disappointed** with our range of fashionable, UV protection clothing for the entire family, available exclusively from *Stupendous Industries*!

Right-margin notes:
- a variety of controlling and emotive words; **must**, **deadly damage**
- paragraphs used to state and elaborate on each point
- a variety of conjunctions; e.g. **So**, **and**
- persuasive language is used so others will agree with the writers point of view; e.g. **Don't delay**, **You won't be disappointed**

Teacher information

- Discussions argue for a particular position and attempt to persuade an audience to share this view. This discussion is in the form of an advertisement trying to persuade people to purchase a particular type of clothing.
- Pupils should read the discussion independently.
- Identify the structural and language features indicated above before the pupils complete the analysis on page 72. Ask pupils to identify examples of controlling and emotive words and conjunctions in the text.
- Teachers should hold a class discussion on some appropriate issues the pupils could write discussions, in the form of advertisements, about. Make a list of topics for later use.
- Select one of these suggestions to model the planning and writing of a discussion using the framework on page 73. The pupils can then follow this example to plan and write their discussions.
- Pupils could display their discussion with a colourful illustration of their product. (Display)
- Pupils could write discussions in conjunction with a unit about the media and advertising. (Context)
- Pupils can give their discussions as oral presentations to other members of the class. (Purpose/Audience)

Answers

Page 72
1. Teacher check
2. *Stupendous Industries* has just released its brand new, innovative range of clothing!
3. (a) Paragraph 1 — *Stupenda clothes* are made from cloth which provides UV protection.

    Paragraph 2 — *Stupenda clothes* can be made into any type of clothing and come in fashionable colours.

    Paragraph 3 — *Stupenda clothes* come in all sizes to fit the whole family.

    Paragraph 4 — Family pets may soon be able to wear clothing made from *Stupenda cloth*.

   (b) Teacher check
   (c) – (d) Teacher check
4. Teacher check

Gals and guys!

Are you the outdoors type—an active person who loves the fresh air and sunshine? Do you live for the sun, sand and surf but are conscious of the dangers of too much exposure to the sun? Do you love spending time in the great outdoors, soaking up the natural beauty of the world around you? Then you must not miss this! Our product is created especially to help you enjoy life in the sun but prevent the deadly damage it can cause. *Stupendous Industries* has just released its brand new, innovative range of clothing!

This extensive range of clothing has been created from exhaustively researched, designed and trialled material. This revolutionary material is guaranteed to resist UV rays, allowing the wearers to spend as much time in the sun as they wish without suffering any damage from these harmful rays. Years of research at the prestigious Yalumbi Institute have finally resulted in the development of this lifestyle-changing product! Imagine being able to spend all weekend in the sun without any skin damage! How practical it is as well for people who spend most of their working lives outside! Landscapers, bricklayers, road workers—all will benefit from wearing clothing made from *Stupenda cloth*™! Employers will want to purchase clothing in this range to protect ALL their workers!

Not only is *Stupendous clothing* UV resistant, but it may also be fashioned into any type of clothing imaginable! Shirts, trousers, hats, jackets, skirts and dresses are all available in *Stupenda cloth*™. It is available in every conceivable colour of the rainbow—particularly the most fashionable colours of the year—jade, aqua and peach! What a bonus! Imagine a whole wardrobe of clothing in fashionable, easy-care, colour-coordinated, protective material!

Stupendous Industries makes its clothing range to fit all sizes. So now mothers can protect their children and wear equally protective clothing in fashionable designs and colours! What a cost-saver! Fashionable and good for your skin! The whole family will benefit from wearing clothing selected from the *Stupendous clothing* range made from *Stupenda cloth*™!

Stupendous Industries is also soon to release an exclusive range for that easily forgotten member of the family—the family pet! Soon your beloved feline or canine could be adorned in kitty coats and hats or doggy shades and jackets and be protected from sun exposure! This exclusive range will only be available through email order.

Don't delay! Find your nearest stockist and purchase your choice of *Stupendous Industries* clothing today! You won't be disappointed with our range of fashionable, UV protection clothing for the entire family, available exclusively from *Stupendous Industries*!

Use the discussion on page 71 to complete the page.

1. Title

Write an interesting new title.

2. Introduction

Write the most important sentence from the introduction.

_____

_____

3. Arguments

(a) Write a brief summary of the argument given in each paragraph of this section.

Paragraph 1	Paragraph 2
Paragraph 3	Paragraph 4

(b) Complete the sentences.

   (i) The strongest argument is given in paragraph ☐

   (ii) The weakest argument is given in paragraph ☐

(c) Write another argument for use in this discussion.

_____

_____

_____

(d) Write one sentence which has both controlling and emotive words and includes a conjunction.

4. Conclusion

Tick the boxes.

(a) The arguments are summarised. ☐   (b) An evaluative comment is given. ☐

1. Plan a discussion about a particular product you would like to sell.

Title

Introduction

Arguments

Conclusion

2. Write your discussion.

3. Edit your work.